A SINGLE DARING ACT

*Connor Travis in the South American Republic of Paraguay
and the Gran Chaco War in the years 1932 and 1933*

GARTH CAMERON

SJ&S

Street Jackson & Stuart
P O Box 6238
Dunedin North
Dunedin 9059
NEW ZEALAND

streetjacksonstuart@gmail.com
+64 27 622 8428

ISBN 978-0-473-55764-5. Softcover
ISBN 978-0-473-55765-2. Kindle

Cover: illustration and design: Steven Heyen
https://stevenheyenart.com
information@stevenheyenart.com
+61 2 8969 6306

Editor's Note

One afternoon in early 2020, I was walking past Haywards Auction House. On a whim, I went in to find an auction in full swing. The room was crowded, the list of items was long. I noticed two large tin trunks, the kind of waterproof, insect-proof trunks that well-heeled travellers used in the days of travel by steamship and railway. Each one had *365574 Flight Lieutenant. C. Travis* painted on its side in faded lettering. I bid for them and won, without being sure what I would use them for.

When I went to pick the trunks up, the counter was crowded, the clerks were busy. I paid and went to carry the trunks out to my car, only to find that they were too heavy for one man. Looking inside, I found each was full of papers, including typescript in bundles, notebooks, folders, and the like. I had wrongly assumed they were empty. I talked to the harassed clerk. He said that the owner had found them when clearing out the attic of a house he had bought. He had no interest in the trunks or their contents.

I hired a truck and two men who loaded the trunks and put them in a corner of my garage. There they stayed until the southern hemisphere winter arrived, the days shortened, and I had the time to examine my find.

What I found was the record of a long, eventful life. Connor Travis appeared to have gone everywhere and done everything a man could do. His father was an engineer, his mother a novelist and artist. He studied law, became a criminal lawyer, learned to fly.

He sought adventure, which usually meant flying in some of the most remote corners of the world. He participated in little-known events, often in little-known places.

At the age of a hundred and one, he decided to record some of his adventures. He had a sharp mind, a good memory, and could refer to an array of documents. His memoir grew to five thousand pages of typescript. I could find no evidence that he had ever sought a publisher.

The manuscript was structured so that each episode in his life was a complete story, and this book is one of those stories: his time in Paraguay in 1932 and 1933.

Garth Cameron
Dunedin
New Zealand
6 August 2021

DEDICATION

This book is dedicated to my grandfather
53575 Private William James Cameron
Auckland Regiment
New Zealand Division
France & Flanders 1917-1918

Chapter One
A City. 12 January 1932

Robert Herbert Scott, who was sentenced to death for the murder of Gwendoline Kathleen Murray, aged 12 at Makaraka on January 28, will be hanged at Mount Eden gaol at 8 am on Thursday next.

– *Stratford Evening Post*. 14 April 1924

Connor Travis. Deckhand. Signed on.
– Ship's Articles, SS *Eden*. Port Chalmers. 2 June 1931

Docked, East Wharf, Bahia de Asunción, Port of Asunción. Finished with engines. Voyage to date. Since sailing from Port Chalmers on 3 June 1931, we have steamed 14,456 nautical miles in 74 days and 14 hours and touched at Bluff, Port Taranaki, Nouméa, Papeete, Valparaíso, Callao, Punta Arenas, Montevideo, Buenos Aires & Asunción.
– B. Hilder, Master. Logbook, SS *Eden*. 5 January 1932

Arrived yesterday. Steamer SS Eden, *of 413 GRT Campbell & Co. registered in Port Chalmers. Seven days out of Buenos Aires with a general cargo consigned to the Casado Company. We understand that the Casado Company is negotiating the purchase of the vessel.*
– *El Liberal*, Asunción. 6 January 1932

I sat outside the Café Indio under the awning while a hot rain sluiced off the canvas onto the shingle and mud of the street.

A Spanish edition of Joseph Conrad's *Nostromo*, a Spanish–English dictionary, and my journal were open in front of me, although I was not thinking about *Nostromo* or the town of Sulaco. I was thinking about twelve-year-old Gwendoline Kathleen Murray and Robert Herbert Scott, the man who had been hanged for her murder.

Scott was not a likeable man. The learned King's Counsel and I had done our best to save his life. Duty and principle demanded that we do so. At the trial, we had put the Crown to the proof and the KC had cross-examined skilfully. Our theory of the case was that our client had killed the victim, but the facts amounted to manslaughter, not murder. Death by hanging was mandatory for murder but not for manslaughter. The KC reminded me of a toad upon a rock, croaking, and all the more effective for it. He talked to the jury, not down to them. I took notes and cross-examined the less important witnesses. The intentions of the accused, the precise cause of death, and the voluntariness of the confession had been challenged, but to no avail.

The jury retired for less than an hour and returned with a verdict of guilty of murder. After the verdict, the court was adjourned. The registrar called the case twenty minutes later. The judge returned to the bench, wearing a black cap over his wig, and sentenced the prisoner to be hanged by the neck until he was dead.

After Scott was sentenced, the learned King's Counsel and I went to talk to Scott's wife. We stood in the corridor of the Supreme Court, still dressed in barrister's rig, horsehair wigs, white shirts with high collars, white tapes, black bar jackets and robes, black trousers, and black shoes. She clung to a sleeve of the KC's robe, repeating over and over, 'But he hasn't done anything. He hasn't done anything.'

What do you say to the wife of a man who had raped and murdered a young girl and was soon to be put to death?

The Court of Appeal dismissed the appeal and the Executive Council declined to grant clemency. So, at eight o'clock in the morning of a cold and drizzly day, they took the prisoner from his cell in Mount Eden Prison and hanged him, and who could say that they were wrong?

Gwendoline was a bright girl, growing up on a small farm near Gisborne on the East Coast of the North Island. Her father had been badly wounded at Gallipoli in August 1915, and resettled on a small farm, barely able to provide a living. Gwendoline went barefoot but was top of her class and spent hours in the school's small library. She had dreamed of exploring the world, being a teacher and writing a famous novel.

Gwendoline and Scott had been dead for eight years and I tried not to think about them.

* *

At Café Indio in Asunción, I was brushing up on my Spanish. My mother was Spanish and my father a Scottish New Zealander. When I was growing up in New Zealand, one day a week I had spoken Spanish with my mother and father, and had read books and newspapers in the language, but until a few months ago, I had not visited a country where Spanish was spoken. My copy of *Nostromo* was battered; I had bought it cheap in a bookshop in Valparaiso. Each country in Latin America spoke a slightly different version of Spanish, which were not quite the same as my mother's or the Spanish in the novel. I enjoyed learning some of the nuances of the local version. Occasionally I heard an unfamiliar, beautiful language, but only the peasants and labourers spoke it. I was told that it was Guarani, the language the Spanish conquistadors encountered when they arrived in this region in the early 1500s.

An attractive, tall, slim woman arrived and sat a few tables away. She was about thirty, with a fair complexion, blue eyes, and straight blonde hair cut short.

A man I knew slightly arrived, smiled and nodded. I asked if he would like to join me for a beer. He was José Diaz, a rare bird indeed, a customs official who was competent, diligent but not officious. He was also one of those people we think of as a good conversationalist because they are happy to listen at least half of the time. He had never travelled outside Paraguay and had no desire to do so but was interested in the outside world. His occupation meant that, from time to time, he met people with interesting stories to tell. The stamps in my passport told him that I had travelled to many countries in the past few years.

He ordered, sat down, and we exchanged pleasantries. He said, 'What were you doing in China?'

I was ready for the question. When I left China, I had decided that I would tell only part of the truth. The full story might not be believed, and I was not sure that my activities were morally justified, so I said, 'I was a draftsman.'

'Who did you work for?'

'The company that operates trams, that is, streetcars, in the French Concession in Shanghai.'

'What are the French doing in China?'

'It's complicated.'

'I have plenty of time.'

'The Chinese Empire was crumbling and militarily weak in the nineteenth century. It still is. European armies and navies were more powerful. The Japanese also saw opportunities. Several countries imposed treaties that guarantee extraterritorial rights. France is one of the countries that benefits. Part of Shanghai is controlled by France.'

José thought about that. 'How do you come to be in Paraguay? I ask everyone that. At least, everyone who might have a good story to tell.'

'I arrived back in New Zealand to find it in the grip of economic depression. It is already being called the Great Depression. There was no work for me.' I did not say that I meant that there was no work for me practising either of my professions, or that my connections would have got me some low-paid, boring job if I had wanted it. Or that I had enough money saved from my time in Great Britain and China to live in reasonable comfort for at least a year.

'Things are bad. Labourers on government-subsidised work schemes have only one set of clothes. If they wear these out, they can't replace them. They take sugar bags, cut holes for their heads and arms, and wear them to protect their clothes. Farmers can't pay their mortgages, so the Government has stopped banks from foreclosing. But the banks will only extend the bare minimum credit necessary. They make the farmers prepare detailed budgets. They go over them with a fine-tooth comb. One farmer I know included two toothbrushes in his budget, one for him and one for his wife. The bank manager asked if they could not get by with one. No wonder people hate banks and bankers.'

José looked unimpressed. 'Most Paraguayans live in abject poverty, and always have. Most of them don't know what a toothbrush looks like.' He paused, then went on, 'If you think working conditions are bad in New Zealand, let me tell you a story.

'Foreign companies own vast tracts of the Chaco. These companies rule factory towns and act like nation states. Puerto Pinasco is a good example. It is owned by a North American company, the International Products Corporation, and employs about three thousand, which makes it the biggest employer in the Republic. The only people who live in Puerto Pinasco are employees of the company. The only shop in town is the company store. The workers are paid in scrip, redeemable only in the company store to buy goods at inflated prices, they work long hours, and conditions are dangerous. Back in 1927, the workers tried to organise a union and went on strike, demanding better pay and conditions. The company called in the Army and the strike was broken by force. The soldiers opened fire, killing about twenty of the workers and wounding many more. Nothing changed. Indians attracted to the company towns are regarded as less than human and are treated that way. Access to alcohol has resulted in them rapidly becoming completely debauched, selling their women and girls into prostitution.'

That kind of event clearly did not bother him much because he changed the subject, and said, 'Tell me more about your voyage.'

'My hometown is the city of Dunedin, in the South Island of New Zealand. It is a port, but most ships dock at Port Chalmers, a short train ride to the north. One evening I was playing poker and one of the players was the first mate of a coaster, SS *Eden*. He told me that one of the crew had got drunk, and on his way back to the ship he fell down some stairs. He broke some bones and would be in the hospital for a least a month. They were short-handed. I was stuck with nothing very interesting to do. I had only been to sea as a passenger, and I thought some time working on a ship would be a learning experience. So I did what they call a "pierhead jump". Less than a day after hearing that there was a vacancy, I had talked to the captain, signed the ship's articles, said my goodbyes, got my trunks, and was aboard *Eden* as it sailed through the heads of the Otago Harbour to the open sea, the Southern Ocean.'

'Southern Ocean?'

'Technically it is the South Pacific, but usually, the enormous cold and windy portion is called the Southern Ocean. Our first stop was Bluff, which is as drab as it sounds, then Port Taranaki in the North Island. *Eden* found a cargo there bound for Nouméa, in French New Caledonia. I could have signed off, but it is hot there and it sounded a bit glamorous, so I stayed on.'

'Was it what you expected?'

'Not bad. The usual ugly wharves, the grog shops, and the brothels. But I had the time to tour the coasts and the interior. A great place, if you are wealthy and French. We landed our cargo and looked for another. The company that owns *Eden* was struggling. The captain's instructions were to take any opportunity to obtain a cargo that would pay enough to cover costs until economic conditions improved. I became the supercargo, a sort of business manager for the ship. In exchange for a small commission, I helped the captain find a cargo. I have learned that many deals are done in social contexts. I play poker and sure enough, a few weeks after arriving, one of the players mentioned a promising opportunity. There was a warehouse full of cheap consumer goods, unsaleable in Nouméa. The French owners were near bankrupt and could not afford all the freight costs. A deal was struck, the French company would pay fifty percent of the freight, and *Eden* would take the cargo to Tahiti. The agents would try to sell it. If the cargo sold, *Eden* would earn the second half of the freight plus a percentage of the sale price.'

'What happened?'

'It was a major risk. We had to trust their good faith and the deal was settled with a handshake. The down payment covered basic expenses, insurance, coal, wages due. And we had been offered a small cargo to pick up in Papeete and take to Valparaiso, in Chile. We landed the cargo in Papeete and sailed for Chile. Months later we had a telegram from head office. The company had received the balance due. This was the first profitable voyage in a long time.'

'Isn't Papeete to Valparaiso a long haul for a small steamer?'

'Indeed, it is. Without careful planning, we might have run out of fuel a long way from anywhere. The captain and the first mate spent many hours with the *Admiralty Ocean Passages for the World* volumes and their wind and current charts. They decided that the small cargo meant we had the space to ship enough extra coal. Steaming at the most efficient speed and using an indirect route would get us there safe and sound. I sat in on the discussions and learned some very interesting things. The voyage was a dirty one until the excess coal had been used and we could clean up. After that, we just counted the days and soon it was certain that we would arrive with coal to spare. Next, we found a cargo for Callao, then one for Punta

Arenas, and one for Montevideo. Finally, there were cargoes for Buenos Aires and Asunción.'

> *Telegram from Head Office confirms freight charges have been paid and the client consignee may land the cargo. The Casado Company is interested in purchasing SS* Eden. *My instructions are to remain at Asunción pending the outcome of negotiations between the agents of Campbell & Co. and Casado's head office at Buenos Aires. All hands to remain on the articles and live aboard.*
>
>   – B. Hilder, Master. Logbook, SS *Eden*. 15 January 1932

'How long are you staying?'

'Uncertain. The company has decided to sell the ship. I think that here is as good a place as any to get a good price. Otherwise, we wait for a cargo.'

We had had a few beers during this conversation and my friend looked at his watch, we agreed to meet up later that week, he made his goodbyes and left.

Chapter Two
The River. 18 January 1932

At home, it would have been a cool, dry ten to fifteen degrees Celsius, but here it was around thirty-five, the humidity approaching a hundred percent, the air like a damp towel, my clothes a hot poultice.

The market was nearby, and I bought two pairs of loose-fitting trousers, three oversize cotton shirts, and a broad-brimmed straw hat.

I enjoyed dressing casually after my years in uniform. I wore my new clothes, kept to the shady side of the streets, and spent much of my time reading in a café in a side street not far from the docks, chatting to the Italian owner when business was light. He assured me that the weather would likely continue to be hot, more rain would fall, and the humidity would increase. He cheerfully explained that the weather could change suddenly, bringing a pampero — strong, frigid, southerly winds — and an accompanying major drop in temperature and humidity.

I had bought a map and guidebook, and when I was not grappling with Conrad and the city's newspapers, I systematically explored the city, at first on foot, and then by electric trams that sparked and swayed and squealed along rutted and potholed streets. Some of the trams were steam-powered, hissing and clanking like miniature trains.

I found a dockside bar, with sawdust on the floor and bottles of pickled onions and bowls of pig's trotters on the counter, where I drank foaming tankards of dark Pilsen beer. One evening I met a wharfie. He insisted that I borrow his bicycle and keep it for as long as I needed it.

From then on, I took the bike with me on the tram and went to the end of each line and rode off, exploring the city.

My impression was that Asunción had been planned as a great city and had been laid out with neat rectangles of streets, but there had never been the money to finish all the major buildings or even seal all the streets and roads. Those that were sealed, were usually finished in rough cobble. I found a building not on my map and which had no obvious purpose. It was large and unfinished with a high cupola, surrounded by scaffolding. There were no workers and the building and scaffolding had started to decay.

The Presidential Palace was enormous and U-shaped, with a high central tower, and painted a vivid white. A large flag of red, white, and blue horizontal stripes flew from a flagstaff fifteen metres high. The seal of the República was at its centre and I noticed that the seal was different on each side. Just one of the quirky things I had noticed about the city and its people. There must have been some special event on, as enormous sheets of red, white, and blue fabric stretched from the front of each wing and the same colours were wrapped around the pillars supporting the portico. I realised that the back of the Palace was the ugly edifice I had noticed, on the bluff, overlooking the port.

I found Congress, the hospitals, churches, and shady plazas. I walked along dirt footpaths, past humble dwellings on narrow streets, and grand houses on broad, tree-lined boulevards. There were cars and a few trucks and many carts with oversized wheels, pulled by horses, donkeys or bullocks. At the central market, the carts came and went. Girls smoking cheroots rode side-saddle, leading strings of mules with packs on their backs. Trucks delivered slabs of ice to the big houses, and water was sold in the street from carts drawn by old, undernourished horses. One day I saw a man on an overloaded and emaciated donkey, delivering milk. He ladled milk out of a huge can and into metal containers held out by the housewives.

The women walked proud and erect, with the comportment of princesses, carrying all manner of burdens on their heads, from small loaves of bread to large milk churns. It was not unusual to see a girl with a milk churn on her head, carrying a second one in her hand, and one or two smaller ones in her other hand.

Each plaza had a special population. Some had stylishly dressed men and women, taking the air in the cool of the evening. Others had many beggars, predominantly men, a few of whom were very old with deeply tanned faces and limbs missing. Down by the river, Indians sold poorly made handicrafts or simply begged. The citizens of the city did not appear to notice them.

It was clear that Paraguay was poor and that many of her citizens lived in poverty, but I could not tell whether they were happy or sad. Some wore sad expressions, but the young girls laughed and chattered, as young girls do everywhere.

One day I walked past a row of shops and offices, boarded up and empty. A dealer in motorcycles, a hairdresser, a lawyer, and a furniture showroom. A poor country made poorer by the crash of the New York stock market and the worldwide economic depression. Something caught my eye, and I went back a few steps and looked through a gap in the boards nailed across the front of the motorcycle shop. The interior was dripping with water and ferns and lush green grass carpeted the floor. A vine wrapped itself around a partly disassembled motorcycle.

* *

At the Courts of Justice, a murder trial was in progress. Entry was by way of a great iron door, guarded by two youthful soldiers, each carrying a rifle. The court was divided in two by a low wooden fence and spectators stood behind it; the public area had no seats. Defence counsel was speaking, and it was clear that the defendant had killed a man, with a machete no less, but should be excused because the deceased had propositioned the defendant's wife. From time to time the judge yawned and lit another cigarette.

I chatted with a fellow spectator who told me that murderers used to be executed by firing squad and that the sentence was carried out in public. Executions drew a huge crowd. He also told me that sentences of death were usually commuted to life imprisonment and that there had not been an execution for some years. He sounded a little disappointed.

* *

I decided to leave and roamed the streets in search of a bookstore.

The city seemed uncannily like my hometown: remote, insular, on a frontier a long way from anywhere. Someone wrote that Asunción has, or at least had, an old-world atmosphere and the sleepy air of repose which most other South American cities seem to lack. That was my experience. Asunción had more churches and fewer hills than home, and Dunedin was richer because of its proximity to the goldfields discovered in the 1860s. Asunción had fewer bookshops.

I found a bookshop on a side street not far from the city centre. The proprietor was a chess fanatic. He convinced me that we should play. We chatted as we played, and he gossiped about the poor state of the economy. Paraguay produced cattle hides, meat that was packed at a plant in the capital, yerba-maté, hardwood, tannin, and little else. Yerba-maté turned out to be leaves that were infused in hot water and drunk through a metal or wooden straw from a globe about twice the size of a cricket ball. It has a mildly narcotic effect and was the national hot drink of choice. The owner insisted on preparing the drink for me. It tasted foul to my untutored palate. He suggested that I drink another globe of the stuff, with heaps of sugar, but that made it taste worse. I was tactful and thanked him but decided it was not for me. From then on, I only drank yerba-maté when it would have been rude to refuse.

* *

One day I was sitting in a deck chair aboard *Eden* when I heard an aero-engine close by. I tracked the sound down to a wharf and looked over to see a boat, a contrivance really, consisting of two floats, a cockpit, an engine driving a pusher propeller, and a rudder behind it. The owner had switched off the engine and was mooring it to a pontoon. We struck up a conversation. He recognised a fellow enthusiast and was happy to while away the time talking about his creation. He asked if I would like a ride. We spent the next hour roaring around the Bay of Asunción at speeds of up to sixty-five kilometres per hour. A refreshing and exciting way to spend time on a hot, muggy day.

* *

One day I spent a few hours sitting on the dock close by the Arsenales de Guerra y Marina, watching as small Navy flying boats were launched from the slipway to fly circuits, taking off and landing from the bay.

One of my acquaintances had told me about a battle in 1537, between Spanish conquistadors and the Guarani, on the lofty hill at Lambaré, 150 metres high. I climbed the hill and looked out over the Rio Paraguay. The confluence of the Rio Paraguay and the Rio Pilcomayo was just visible through the haze to the south-west. The Pilcomayo rose in Bolivia and flowed south-eastwards toward Asunción, dividing the Paraguayan Chaco from Argentina. The Paraguay flowed south and was the border between north-western Argentina and south-eastern Paraguay. The hill was without shade and the heat ended my geographical musings, driving me from the summit and back into the city. I went to my favourite café and settled down to read and write.

There is a Russian proverb that 'a woman is a complete civilisation', and Tolstoy wrote that 'nothing is so important for a young man as the company of intelligent women'. I have found both observations to be true. All my life I have sought out the company of clever women; this time a clever woman sought my company.

I was reading when my train of thought was interrupted. The blonde woman was standing by me. She asked me what I was reading. I asked if she would like to join me for a drink.

'I would.'

I stood up, and she held out her hand. 'Sophia Isabella Garcia Fuentes.' She was tall, almost 1.85 metres, and in her high heels, she was my height.

I shook her hand. 'Connor Travis.'

'Were your parents so poor they could not afford to give you a middle name?'

I laughed. My day had taken a turn for the better.

'Do respectable women while away afternoons in cafés and talk to strangers?'

'This one does, sometimes. What would you like to drink?'

'A cold beer and an espresso.'

'An unusual combination.'

'It is. I drink it when I am people-watching.'

She ordered beers and espressos for both of us. The drinks arrived, and the proprietor left a saucer with the bill on it.

I tried to think of something wise to say but all I could come up with was, 'To Paraguay!'

'To Paraguay. Who are you? You dress like a peasant, but you are not. And you are not Paraguayan. No offence.'

'None taken.'

There was a pause in the conversation, and then she said, 'Are you thinking about who you are?'

'I am a seaman. My ship is in port. We are waiting for cargo, or for the ship to be sold. Where do you fit in? What do you do?'

We were speaking Spanish. She ignored my question. 'A seaman? Not the whole story. A strange accent. You speak very … precisely. A little difficult to understand. Your vocabulary is … archaic … archival. Where did you learn your Spanish?'

'From my mother. Spanish but born in Tunis, in French Tunisia. She grew up speaking Spanish, French, some Arabic. What do you do for a living?'

'You assume that I am not kept, as a wife, as a mistress?'

'Are you?'

'I'm an architect. And an artist. I have a studio and another job.'

'What kind of job?'

'Cartographer and draftsman. At the Geographic Institute.'

'What kind of art?'

'Painting, sketching, woodcuts, linocuts. I studied at the Bauhaus for four years. At Weimar in Germany. Architecture, design, art. I already had modernist leanings. There are a lot of influences on my work. I am starting to develop a style of my own.'

I said, 'Do your countrymen like your art?'

'Some of them buy it.'

I had spent some time in art galleries, and said, 'I have seen some modernist art.'

'Modernist? Which artists?'

'Wassily Kandinsky, Kazimir Malevich and Piet Mondrian.'

'I know Kandinsky; he taught at the Bauhaus. Did you know he was a successful lawyer, and was offered a post as a professor? He would have taught Roman Law. He said no and concentrated on developing his art. Have you seen the work of any others?'

'Yes, but I confess I can't remember their names. They will be in my journal.'

'What were you doing in Europe?'

'A friend and I went on tour from London to Baghdad and back. Doing the modern equivalent of the grand tour.'

We had another drink. And several more. The cold beer and espressos complemented each other delightfully. The conversation became discursive. We talked about art and architecture and Paraguay. We lost count of the drinks and the pile of saucers with their bills grew steadily. She told me that she could follow my Spanish easily, despite its many anachronisms. I asked about Paraguayan literature and art.

'Sometimes we follow international trends. There has been a strong impressionist movement since the turn of the century, some of it is first class. We are a small country, but there are significant writers; no one an outsider would know of though. We are small and unknown and like to be different, mostly.'

'Different?'

'One of only two South American countries to be landlocked. Bolivia is the other. We are remote, from South America, from the world. The capital of Bolivia is about fourteen hundred and fifty kilometres to the north-west. Buenos Aires is more than a thousand kilometres to the south-east. Rio Janeiro is eleven hundred kilometres north-east of here. The rivers were the only practical way to move people and goods in and out of Paraguay. We have a railway to Encarnación on the Rio Parana, just across from Posadas in Argentina. We can take an Argentinian train from there, but most cargo and passengers still come and go by ship. We are an island surrounded by land.'

I thought about this, and said, 'I come from somewhere just as isolated, more isolated in fact, but surrounded by water, lots of water. On the outer rim of an empire. My home overlooks the sea, the Southern Ocean. If you sail due east across that ocean, the next land is nine thousand kilometres away — the coast of Chile.'

'Your first language is English?'

'Yes.'

'The empire is the British Empire?'

'Yes.'

'You are from Australia?'

'No, New Zealand. I live, lived, in Dunedin on the east coast of the South Island. I sometimes took a tram to Saint Kilda Beach and looked due east over the ocean, trying to grasp the fact that the next land was such a very long way away.'

'Tram?'

'Streetcar.'

'And you are not a sailor?'

'I have been for the past six months or so. You can learn a lot about seafaring in six months. Hard, dangerous work. The ship is undermanned because of the Depression, tramping from place to place, never sure of cargo, or earning enough to pay us. So all of us have to pitch in to perform every task — stow cargo, use the winches and derricks, help in the engine room. One of the stokers got drunk and stayed drunk for a week, so I had to work in the stokehold. I learned to stand a watch at the wheel, and how to splice steel cables.'

I showed the palms of my hands, horny and marked with a dozen healed scratches. She took my hands, ran her fingers over them, a curiously intimate act. She said, 'Do you enjoy being a sailor?'

'Not stoking, not in the tropics. A dirty, stinking job at the best of times, but I enjoy acquiring new skills. The captain is a fine seaman and something of an intellectual. He holds an Extra Masters Certificate, a sort of maritime PhD, only a handful of captains do. He is also a historian and studies Polynesian voyagers and makes all kinds of old-time navigational instruments. He helped me brush up on my celestial navigation — position finding by observing the sun, moon, and navigational stars. He also showed me how to use some of the traditional instruments he had made. One of them, the Arab kamal, is just a small, square piece of wood with a knotted string. You grip the string with your teeth, move the wood until the bottom is on the horizon and the top is on the star. The number of knots between your mouth and the kamal gives you the latitude north or south of the port you departed from, and the same for your destination. Surprisingly accurate.'

'What did the crew think of you? Captain's pet?'

'Six of the crew held certificates as officers: two masters, three first mates, and one second mate. They signed on as seamen because those were the only berths they could find. They were better educated than the average seamen but were still rough men. Some of them were suspicious and a bit hostile at first. I shared the fo'c'sle with eight men, but I have a bayonet my father gave me, a souvenir from his service in the Great War. I kept it in its scabbard, in my jumping-off bag. Once a week I took the bayonet out and sharpened it with an oil stone, so sharp I could have shaved with it. A non-verbal message that they should think about before giving me a hard time. I did all the dirty jobs, didn't complain, and kept my mouth shut so they weren't too rough on me.'

'A jumping-off bag?'

'Every sailor has one. Documents, money, a change of clothes, perhaps some concentrated food. In case the ship is suddenly in distress and has to be abandoned quickly. In port, I sometimes rescued crew members when they went out for a wet and a visit to the dockside whorehouses.'

'A wet?'

'To merchant seaman, a serious drinking session is a "wet", alcohol is "neck oil" or "lunatic soup". A ship is a foreign country to landsmen and its inhabitants speak a distinctive dialect. Did you know that the Ancient Greeks were not sure whether to number sailors amongst the living or the dead?'

'I did not.'

'Seamen live lives that are very different from those of landsmen. When strength and teamwork are required, say hauling on lines, they sometimes sing sea shanties, just like in the old sailing ship days. Even in a steamer, many tasks require that kind strength and teamwork.'

'Sing one for me.'

'In a café, in the afternoon, in the middle of your capital city? Better make it another time.'

She laughed and asked, 'Before you were a sailor?'

I thought about the question. She might not believe the complete story. I decided to keep some of my life private. 'I was a lawyer. I worked as a law clerk and studied law part-time. After I was admitted to the bar, I went to work for a learned King's Counsel who practised criminal law. I helped him prepare for trials and was a junior during the proceedings. He was old, and his advocacy was unique, rough but honest. It worked; he was very persuasive.'

'King's Counsel?'

'A senior and skilled barrister, technically an appointment made by the King.'

'Did you always win?'

Laymen always asked that. A difficult question to answer briefly yet truthfully. 'Often. No lawyer wins every case. And how do define a win? A win might be a verdict of not guilty, the client walking free. That rarely happens in homicide cases. It might be persuading a jury that the killing was manslaughter and not murder. Hanging is not the mandatory sentence for manslaughter, the client goes to prison instead of the gallows. You have saved the client's life, an undeniably good result.' I paused. 'A lawyer is only as good as his best point.'

'Best point?'

'When I was a beginner, a wise old barrister explained it to me. A lawyer may be eloquent, persuasive, and have an outstanding knowledge of the law, but he can only win if there is some fact or principle he can hang his hat on. For example, in a criminal trial, the prosecution might prove that a crime has taken place, but the evidence that it was the defendant who committed the crime might be shaky. A witness who says he saw the defendant at the scene might be cross-examined into admitting that while he thinks the man he saw was the defendant, he is not certain. The "best point" the lawyer has is that while a crime was committed, the jury should find that there is a reasonable doubt that the accused was the person seen leaving the crime scene.'

'How many of your clients are innocent?'

'A lawyer can't tell. He can assess the strength of the Crown's evidence, how credible a witness and his evidence will be, the prospects of acquittal or conviction. It is not for a lawyer to determine guilt or innocence. He must not, that is for judges and juries.'

Sophia asked another question that laymen always asked: 'How can you defend guilty men? And women?'

'How can I not? It is my duty. No person should be convicted unless the prosecution proves each element of the offence beyond a reasonable doubt. The lawyers and judges ensure that that rule is always applied. If they stop doing their duty, a cornerstone of liberal democracy is removed, and democracy is fatally damaged. If authority is not kept up to the mark, the rule of law is weakened. A few cases are chilling reminders of why due process must be granted to every defendant.'

'For example?'

'One of our clients had been feuding with another man. There had been violence; it escalated, and our man's cottage was burnt down. Soon afterwards the other man was found dead, in his car, of a single gunshot wound to the temple. Our client was observed in the area around the time of death. The bullet shattered and could not be matched to a particular gun, but our client owned a rifle of the type that was probably used. He was arrested and charged with murder. The circumstantial evidence might have been enough to see him hanged. Then a man came forward. He had been handling a defective rifle in the back of a moving truck. It fired at the very moment the truck passed the deceased's car Not murder, just a bizarre accident.

'Another example was a client whose wife had left him for another man. He had been seen, several times, hanging about in the street where the wife and her lover lived. One night he was seen in the vicinity. An hour or so later the house burnt down; it was arson. The police assumed it was my client. So did I, except a little later a burglar confessed that he had burgled the house and set it on fire to cover his tracks.'

'You are passionate about your work? And a little pompous?'

I smiled back. 'Yes, to both, an occupational hazard. A lawyer needs to talk precisely so there is no ambiguity. All too often it sounds patronising. Often it is, and I do my best not to. If we stop protecting those who are probably guilty, the state will seek out those who are probably innocent. A few guilty men or women walking free is the price of protecting the liberty of all. Do people get a fair trial here?'

'Most of them do. Do you like Paraguay?'

'I don't know it well enough to say yes or no. It is different, exotic.'

'We are proud of being different. Even our languages are different.'

'I have heard some people talking Spanish and another language, one that seems … chirpy, bird-like? I have forgotten what it is called.'

'Guarani. The indigenous language. We are unique in that many of us speak Spanish and Guarani. In most of Latin America, the Spanish settlers and their descendants speak only Spanish.'

'Why is Paraguay different?'

'Paraguay was so isolated that the Spanish settlers intermarried in large numbers. Most of us think of ourselves as Mestizo, Spanish and

Indian. Most educated people speak Spanish and many of them also speak Guarani. Almost half of Paraguayans speak only Guarani.'

I asked about the grand but old and unfinished building with its decaying scaffolding.

'You are talking about the Panteón Nacional de Los Héroes. It was started by President Francisco Solano López in 1863. After his death, there was neither the will nor the money to finish it.'

It had stopped raining. The light was fading. A stack of saucers, each with its bill, stood on the table.

She said, 'I must go. Would you like me to show you the sights, tomorrow?'

'Yes.'

'Can you be here at seven in the morning?'

'I can.'

'See you then. Let's split the bill.'

We paid the bill, and not drunk, but not entirely sober either, I walked home to my ship, past two Paraguayan gunboats.

* *

The next day dawned cool and dry. Sophia was standing beside her car when I arrived, looking decidedly boyish. She was dressed in dungaree pants, a checked cotton shirt, and flat-soled brown lace-up shoes. A blonde Amelia Earhart. 'I hope I have not kept you waiting?'

'Just arrived. I have something special to show you.'

We got into her car, a green-and-black Ford Model A coupé with the top down. In a few minutes, we were at the docks and on a landing stage at the bottom of some wooden steps not far from SS *Eden*. We climbed aboard a small motorboat. Sophia started the outboard engine at the second pull. I cast off we and motored between two ships and out into the Bahia Asunción and on to the Rio Paraguay, heading north.

Sophia waved her hand over the brown surface of the river. 'One of my American friends says that the Rio Paraguay is too thick to drink and too thin to plough.'

I smiled and nodded.

After forty minutes of companionable silence, we saw a small gap in the western bank of the river and turned toward it. Sophia steered through it into a lagoon. She switched off the motor and the boat drifted into a huge field of giant water lilies, all about two metres wide, the surfaces wrinkled like the skin of a lizard and with white and pink flowers. Natural history has never been my strong suit. I was happy to listen as Sophia described the life cycle and aesthetics of the lilies.

'We only see them every four years or so. The flowers last only two days, white on the first, and pink on the second. The plant appears to be free-floating but is connected to the bottom of the lagoon by fragile tendrils. The lily pads and the flowers are buoyant and carry most of the weight. They are called *victoria cruziana*, or *yacaré yrupe*, the Guarani name because the lily pad's surface looks like the skin of a caiman. A small child can stand on one.'

We drifted quietly through the lilies chatting. I said, 'Asunción seems a quiet, friendly place.'

PRESIDENT OF PARAGUAY FORCED TO RESIGN BY RADICAL ELEMENTS

The President of Paraguay, Senior Guggiari, has been forced by Radical elements to resign. His place has been taken by the Vice-President, says the Associated Press correspondent at Asunción. There have been many demonstrations against the President during the last few days, culminating in an attack on the Presidential Palace made by a mob of communists and students on Saturday. The police were obliged to open fire, and twelve persons were killed.

The President was unpopular owing to the conciliatory attitude he adopted regarding the dispute between Paraguay and Bolivia over the Chaco region.
— *The Scotsman,* Edinburgh. 24 October 1931

Sophia looked slightly amused. She said, 'Most of the time. Where would you like to go next?'

'How far is the airfield?'

'Ñu Guasú? About twenty minutes from the docks, the roads are rough.'

'The airfield then?'

'The airfield.'

We headed back to the harbour and the landing stage and tied the boat up.

We returned to the car, drove for twenty minutes and soon we were parked on a slight rise overlooking the airfield, a rectangle of dry grass and bare earth, about a thousand metres on each side. On the boundary furthest from us there was a line of hangars, a tower for airing and drying parachutes, what appeared to be workshops, and a bigger two-storey, white-painted building that I guessed contained offices and classrooms. There were a few aeroplanes parked in front of the hangars and another was pushed out of the hangar as we watched.

I said, 'How long can we stay?'

'As long as you like.'

We spread a rug and sat with our backs to the car. Mechanics were pushing more aeroplanes out of the hangars and preparing them for flight. Engines were started and warmed up, then were run-up to full power, creating miniature dust storms.

I said, 'Someone told me there was a Civil War in 1922 to 1923.'

'There was.'

'Were you in danger?

'I was in Germany, studying.'

In front of the hangars, pilots and observers, clad in overalls, donned parachutes and helmets and climbed aboard their aircraft. The mechanics pulled chocks away from the wheels. Three of the aeroplanes taxied over to the far corner of the airfield and took off toward us. They passed overhead, biplanes painted olive green, the pilot and observer visible in the open cockpits. They had red-white-and-blue striped rudders with a yellow star in the centre. On the wings were red-white-and-blue roundels. I could see that one of the observers was a young man, who smiled and saluted us. One of a generation for whom every flight was an exciting privilege. Three more aircraft took off and passed overhead, fighters — single-seat, parasol-wing monoplanes.

The aircraft formed up into two tight, arrowhead formations, then echeloned right and climbed away to the north-east. I recognised the types and noted the skill with which the aircraft were flown.

Sophia noted my interest. 'Are you a pilot?'

'Yes, my father taught me to fly after he came back from the Great War. He bought a surplus Avro 504K, a two-seat trainer, a leftover from the war. After my training was complete, we converted the front cockpit to take two passengers and went barnstorming in our holidays. Up and down the West Coast of the South Island, landing on beaches and clearings in the bush. The flying kept me sane when I worked in a law office where I was a law clerk.'

'Kept you sane?'

'The pay was a pittance; the partners were rude and demanded slavish deference. This is the traditional way of treating law clerks. It got better as I learned the ropes. Do you have to go to work today?'

'No, day off.'

'Why?'

'I have met a charming man and declared a holiday.'

We watched the flying until midday then returned to the city and made the most of the cool and comfortable weather, walking the streets while Sophia told me about the provenance and architecture of the public buildings. And some of the scandals associated with the apartments. One was about a husband and wife whose thirty years together was war, not marriage. She was seventeen and he thirty-four when they married; he tall and dark, she petite, blue-eyed, and blonde. His lineage went back to the conquistadors, while she was the daughter of Germans who had attempted to set up a colony for pure-blooded Aryans at Nueva Germania in the 1880s. He was volatile. One day he tried to murder his mother and chased her with a pistol, firing many shots but never hitting her. When he was arrested, he persuaded the police that he had attempted suicide and botched it.'

'That does not make any sense. I mean, what was clearly an attempted murder of his mother was now no such thing, and he only intended to kill himself? He was that persuasive?'

'There is more. He had an automatic pistol with a nine-round magazine and had fired thirty-two bullets, meaning he had reloaded at least three times.'

'And the police let him go?'

'He would have been polite, reasonable, and persuasive. The police may have decided he was such a poor shot that he was a danger only to himself; after all, the knife is the weapon of choice in the República. And he had a good family name.'

She thought for a moment then said, 'In Paraguay, politeness is a much-prized virtue. If you ever find yourself in a tight spot, don't get angry, be respectful. Use moderate language.'

'Am I likely to get into a tight spot?'

'I don't know you well enough to know. But you might walk into the middle of a coup or a revolution. Would you like to know what happened to the couple?'

'Yes indeed.'

'She became an artist, while he was a novelist. After years of conflict and countless separations and reconciliations, the couple decided to separate, and they and their lawyers met at his apartment. Halfway through the meeting, he threw acid in her face. Later shot himself in the head. There is more. She moved into his apartment and spent years trying not to look in the mirror. One evening, fourteen years after his suicide, she threw herself from a fourth-floor window. With fatal results.'

We continued our tour of the centre of the city and after walking a few more blocks, she pointed to a three-storey apartment building. 'There is a story associated with that building. There was a society wedding. The bride and groom received many fine presents. One of which was an eighteen-year-old girl. She spent the wedding night with them, in their apartment.'

There was something about the way she told the story that made me ask, 'That wasn't you, by chance?'

She smiled. 'It was. Not by chance, by arrangement.'

'Did you have a say in all this?'

'It was my idea.'

'Did it become a habit?'

'Oh no, you only give a wedding present once.'

She took my hand and held it lightly against her side. The story and the warmth of her body were intimate and mildly erotic.

* *

Around seven that evening we arrived at Sophia's apartment. The apartment consisted of the entire upper floor of what had been a warehouse, divided into large spaces for a combined office and living room, and a kitchen, bathroom, and bedroom. There was a small darkroom. All the rooms, except the bathroom and darkroom, had floor-to-ceiling windows. Each window could be opened wide and there were shutters for the hottest months.

The furniture was spare and modern. The office had a long worktable, paints and brushes, a typewriter, a large drafting board and a stool. Two of the walls were covered in framed works of art, most distinctly modern. Some of the others looked like engraved plates of the type used to illustrate one of the great French encyclopaedias of the eighteenth century. The rear wall was covered in floor-to-ceiling bookshelves and each shelf was full of books. A ladder ran on tracks on the floor and along the upper edge of the top shelf.

I gestured toward the wall of books. 'May I?'

'Of course. I'm going to shower and change.'

I climbed halfway up the ladder and looked along a shelf. It was full of books on art, architecture, and design. Amongst the books in Spanish, French, and German, I recognised several in English. One was Sir Banister Fletcher's *A History of Architecture on the Comparative Method for the Student, Craftsman, and Amateur*. I opened it and found that it was the first edition, published in 1896. An identical copy graced the shelves of my father's study.

Sophia emerged, freshly showered, shoeless, and dressed in a light summer dress with a pattern of stylised dancers in bold colours. She was near thirty and could pass for sixteen. I said, 'Sorry, I am being rude, bookshelves are the first things I notice when I visit a new home.'

She smiled and asked whether I would like something to drink. I chose orange juice; she produced a large glass of it and opened a bottle of red wine for herself.

I had noticed coloured pencil sketches of dancers, all wearing seventeenth-century clothing. I asked about them and she said, 'They are by Leon Bakst, for the Ballet Russe of Paris. They performed all over Europe and North and South America. I saw them perform several times in Europe and struck up friendships with some of the dancers and designers. The sketches were gifts.'

Some of the paintings reminded me of art I had seen in Paris. I asked about them too. 'Yes, they are impressionist, all by Paraguayan artists,' Sophia replied. 'Asunción has a thriving art community. Impressionism took hold here soon after it appeared in France. We are a long way from anywhere, but we still have strong connections with the outside world. International mail arrives almost every day. The Ferrocarril Central del Paraguay ends at Encarnación, and a rail ferry joins it to the Argentinian rail network. Passenger steamers sail from Asunción to Buenos Aires at least twice a week. Steamers arrive from Argentina twice a week. The telegraph connects us with the outside world and our newspapers take in the major wire services, so not much happens in the world that we don't know about.'

We sat on leather sofas, facing each other, and talked. I said, 'One evening I was near the centre of the business district when I heard a piano being played well. Apparently from the second storey of a nondescript commercial building. I found the entrance, walked up the stairs and discovered a large room with tables, chairs, and a long bar with mirrors behind it.'

'Near the central market?'

'Yes.'

'The Café Eiffel?'

'Yes. So Parisian, I half expected to see Toulouse-Lautrec.'

'Yes indeed, very French. How long did you stay?'

'Long enough to join a poker game for a few hours. I met a few interesting people. One of them a Paraguayan who spoke English with an Australian accent. His name is Sandy Murray, and after the game broke up,

I had several drinks with him. He had a story to tell about how he came to be here. In the 1890s, William Lane and a group of Australian socialists emigrated here to establish the perfect society. I have heard of people emigrating to Australia for that reason, but this is the first time I have heard of people leaving Australia to make a perfect society.'

Sophia said, 'Every Paraguayan has heard the story. Lane's version of utopia consisted of a community at Nueva Australia, where there was no personal property, no alcohol, no dancing, and rigid adherence to his rules. The rules were anti-pleasure, and it soon failed. Most of the Australians abandoned socialism, moved to Villarica, and founded another Australian colony.'

'Yes, Sandy was born in Villarica. He manages an estancia somewhere in the Chaco.'

'Did you win at cards?'

'I broke even. There was a woman, curly brunette hair, about thirty-five, White Russian I think, playing and singing. When I arrived, she was performing 'Mac the Knife' from Bertolt Brecht's *Three Penny Opera*. Playing it very well. I stayed longer than I intended.'

'I know her; she is very good.'

'Do you know everyone in Paraguay?'

'Paraguay, Asunción that is, is a village. There are so few well-educated and cultured men and women, that I would expect to know someone like her.'

'And she is Russian?'

'Yes. Valentina Raskova, in self-exile since the Reds won the Russian Civil War. The Bolsheviks killed all her family.'

'The café was crowded, all men, except the pianist and the women behind the bar. All the women were strikingly good-looking. There were two tables of men playing cards, and it is more than just a café. After she finished her set, one of the women came over and whispered in her ear.

She disappeared through a side door. One of the men followed her out. About an hour later she returned and played another set. I didn't recognise the pieces, but they were very good. I had a great night.'

'You would have guessed that it is a combined café, gentlemen's club, and brothel.'

'I did. The most sophisticated I have seen.'

'And you have seen many?'

'You mean brothels? Yes, I have seen some.'

'And been a customer?'

'No. Not on moral grounds. Personal, instead. I am not prepared to cross the line between friendship sex and commercial sex. I had one slightly bizarre experience where I was invited to pay for sex. This is how it happened. One day I met a woman on the street, we chatted. She gave me her phone number and I rang her, and we went out on a date. Soon we were in a sexual relationship. After a few weeks, she told me that I only took her out because I wanted to have sex with her. She proposed that I could have sex without taking her out if I gave her the money I would have spent on dinner and drinks.'

'And did you?'

'No. She must have realised that she was defining herself as a whore. Not only did she change her mind, but she would also not talk to me and cut me dead on the street.'

'Were you disappointed?

'Not really, it was like being given a set of encyclopaedias and then being asked to buy another set.'

Sophia laughed.

I said, 'I met a man who told me he was in the lace business.'

'Ñandutí lace, the Jesuits introduced the manufacture of it. It is mostly produced by individual artisans, working at home. Your friend is probably a middleman who buys it from them and supplies the retailers. The lace is unique in combining Guarani and Spanish decorative themes.'

I said, 'And the piano singer. She is a whore, but educated and cultured?'

'Yes. She came from a family of successful creatives: novelists, an architect, musicians. She studied at the Conservatory in Saint Petersburg. She does what she needs to do to survive. There are strict rules at the Café Eiffel. The men never break them because if they do, they are excluded from one of the best clubs in the city. If a woman is going to whore, she might as well do it there. She and I have talked a lot about life choices and compromises. My mother made them, I made them, Valentina made them. She says that we all sell parts of ourselves; it is only a question of which parts.'

I said, 'Lawyers certainly do. We comply with the ethical rules, most of us are scrupulous. But ethical or not, we often must do good things for bad people. If that isn't selling a part of yourself, I don't know what is.'

'Some men see a woman like Valentina and are contemptuous, or even use her services and despise her. You are not judgmental, I like that.'

'My parents were free thinkers and were slow to judge anyone.'

I suddenly remembered someone I had seen at the Café Eiffel. A man of about thirty, wearing a black suit, white shirt, and black tie. He had a newspaper and cup of coffee in front of him but wasn't drinking or reading. He was simply waiting. I had seen him before. At the Italian's café, soon after my hours of watching the naval flying boats at the arsenal. Perhaps he just liked spending time in cafés, as I did. And the capital did not have all that many people who could afford to while away time that way.

I asked the question I had wanted to ask since Sophia introduced herself. 'So, how does a blue-eyed, blonde with a German first name and a Spanish family name, come to be a Paraguayan?'

'I was born in Colonia Nueva Germania, like the wife I told you about. It is a settlement about three hundred kilometres north-east of Asunción. My parents were German peasants, settlers recruited in 1887 by Doctor Ludwig Bernhard Förster and his wife, Elisabeth Nietzsche Förster, sister of the philosopher–historian Friedrich Wilhelm Nietzsche. Their vision was of a socialist community where a utopia could be created, and all would share in the bounty. And it would be purely Aryan, free of Jews.'

'What is an Aryan?'

'German racists are vague on that point. Anyone they like the look of is an Aryan, ideally blonde and blue-eyed, Scandinavian, anyone else is "dross", mud people. They use that definition freely.'

'Did the settlers create a utopia?'

'No. The settlers built a fine mansion for Doctor Förster and his wife, but the rest of them had to live in hovels. The soil was poor, and disease killed many settlers. The first death by disease had occurred on the Rio Parana before the settlers had even reached Paraguay, a young girl. They buried her on the riverbank. Later victims included my father when I was nine years old. Doctor Förster shot himself in the head in 1889, and his wife returned to Germany about 1896, supposedly to recruit replacements for those who had died and the many who had drifted away. But she never returned. Last I heard, she had been adopted by right-wing, anti-Semitic extremists. But I think that Nietzsche's sister has appropriated her brother's writings and ideas in a way that he might not have approved of. If you read him carefully, his philosophy is nuanced in a way that many readers and admirers either don't notice or choose to ignore.'

'How did the daughter of an impoverished peasant woman come to be an educated, sophisticated woman, an architect?'

'My mother was relatively young and still attractive when my father died. And of a practical turn of mind. She made an arrangement with the son of a local landowner, a Paraguayan, rich by the standards of the countryside. He installed us in a small house on the estate and made sure we ate well and dressed well. He did not wish to marry; my mother met his needs. He treated my mother, and me, with courtesy and respect. They came to like each other. He found a place for me in a good Catholic high school here in Asunción. Thanks to him, I met a man, many years older than me. He proposed to me. I was eighteen and he was seventy. I was his third wife.'

I must have looked judgmental.

'You disapprove?'

'No.'

'He did not like women; he liked beautiful young men. Paraguayan society strongly disapproves of such desires. His wives were window dressing. I entertained and accompanied him to social events. A good name, a wife, and a modicum of discretion kept him safe. Everyone knew of course, but he made sure that they never had to confront his desires. I liked him, we were friends and we read and talked about literature and ideas. He died suddenly in 1921, leaving his entire estate to me. I still miss him. I could have lived the rest of my life without working but I wanted more. So I went to the Bauhaus.'

'Hence the modernist paintings on these walls?'

'Yes. The courses included painting and sculpture but leaned more towards industrial design and architecture, which I concentrated on.'

'Is the Bauhaus at Dessau?'

'It is now; it was at Weimar when I was there. It moved to Dessau the year after I graduated.'

'I asked because the Junkers factory is at Dessau, and they make very modern, all-metal aircraft.'

'I know. We spent two days touring the factory and having the design and building process explained.'

'Did you fly?'

'Three times. I loved it. I wish there were a flying school here. If there was, I would learn to fly.'

'Did you like Germany?'

'Yes. But there was hyperinflation while I was there. Money died. It hit the middle class hard, wiping out years of savings by thrifty men and women who had looked forward to comfortable retirements. Of course, it wiped out debt, which could be paid off in valueless money. There was also an undercurrent of extremism and violence in the aftermath of losing the war, and the post-war revolutions. It got worse after the currency crashed. The far-left and the far-right became more extreme, and things have not completely settled down.'

'And the Bauhaus?'

'I enjoyed school, the teachers were first-rate, the social life was wonderful.'

'Do you ever go back to Colonia Nueva Germania?'

'No. It is a collection of hovels, of poor, illiterate peasants. It was fought over by both sides in the Civil War, the one in the 1920s. Our only connection would be our German roots, but that is not enough. My mother died in my last year of high school; she was my only link to the place.'

'Were you in Paraguay during the Civil War?'

'No, in Germany.' She paused, and then went on, 'Did you know that the German and Australian settlements are only two of the many attempts by emigrants to create something in Paraguay that they could not create in their homelands?'

'Vaguely.'

'Yes, one of them was another colony of Germans. Those Germans did better than my forebears, some of them became successful businessmen, lawyers, politicians. We have vegetarians from Finland, and

Italians, Mennonites from Russia and Canada, farmers from Brittany. The Mennonites will certainly stick it out and stick together, but the others, those who don't go home, disperse into the general population. You are bound to meet some more. Paraguay is the home of failed utopias.'

She paused again, then said, 'Tell me about your parents.'

'My father is a New Zealander of Scottish stock. Less dour than his forebears.'

We were speaking English, and she said, 'Dour?'

I tried to explain. 'Serious, always expecting the worst but striving for the best. Actually, the Scots are not dour, it is a stereotype put about by the English.' I thought for a moment, and added, 'Scotland is more advanced culturally than England. For example, the Scots have a strong belief in the value of education. They look down on the English. Almost every Scot is literate, and Scotland provided schools for boys and girls for a hundred years before the English got around to it. That is why if you go to the engine room hatch of almost any steamer, and shout "Jock!" or "Mac!", you will usually get a reply. When steamers first came into service, they needed literate and numerate men to build and maintain the engines, and there was a much bigger pool of Scotsmen for the jobs than Englishmen. With a university-educated Scot as a father, there was never any doubt that I would finish high school and go on to university.'

'Your mother. You said she was Spanish?'

'A writer and an artist. Her Arabic calligraphy is beautiful.'

'Is that where you got your creative impulse from? I saw you with sketchbooks in the café?'

'Partly. My father is an engineer, I learned drafting from him and sketching from my mother. My mother is also a novelist.'

'A successful one?'

'Yes. My father has contacts in publishing in London. One of the contacts recommended an agent who specialised in translations of

European fiction. She sent her first manuscript — in Spanish — to him and asked for his assistance. Eight months later she received a contract, the galleys for correction, together with a cheque for seventy-five guineas and an invitation to submit further manuscripts. The agent had sent her work to a publisher in Barcelona who read it and loved it.'

Sophia looked intrigued. 'What does she write about?'

'Peasant girls and servants who prosper and have romantic lives. One of her characters lead a band of guerrillas against the French in 1808 and married a prince. Another saved the life of a princess in the days of El Cid and became her lady-in-waiting and lifelong friend. Sometimes my mother contributes illustrations for their dust jackets and chapter headings. Did I tell you I was born in Shanghai?'

'No, you didn't.'

'My father spent a year in England studying advanced metallurgy. On the way to a new job in China, his ship had mechanical trouble and had to dock at Tunis for repairs. He met my mother in the market, where she was sketching. They were married within the week, and a week after that they sailed for China. My father had a contract to work on the building of streetcar lines in the French Concession. My older brother was born ten months to the day after they met.'

Sophia finished her bottle of wine and opened another. We talked about what mattered to each of us, the things that made our lives meaningful. She described the Bauhaus and men and women who taught or studied there. I talked about my summer holidays from high school and working on the Port Craig Timber Company's narrow-gauge railway, repairing the track and the wooden trestles over the ravines and creeks. Stoking the small locomotives as they rattled along tracks lined with giant ferns and great trees. One of the trestles was the longest and highest in the southern hemisphere. The railway was used to haul giant kauri trees from the depths of the forests to the wharf where they were loaded on the steamers. I had to grow up quickly. Boy to man in a few harsh lessons. After working there, away from familiar places and people, after conquering homesickness, I never felt it again.

She said, 'Are you interested in Paraguay's history and destiny?'

'History? Destiny, that sounds portentous. Of course.'

'I will talk to the Director of the Geographic Institute. I am sure he will talk to you. All Paraguayans want foreigners to understand our history,' she said, and paused before adding, 'Conditions must be rough on your boat … ship? What do you do when bath time comes around?'

'For the past six months, I have had to make do with a bucket of hot water from the engine room, yellow soap, a bucket of cold water to rinse with, and a threadbare towel. On deck. I went to a dingy bathhouse in Callao. Lots of soap and as much hot water as I wanted, but still no privacy.'

'Would you like a shower? The hot water cylinder was intended to serve the whole building. Now it's only me. Let the water run as long as you like.'

I realised how enormously attractive the idea was. 'Yes, I would.'

'There are a fresh towel and a bar of soap next to the shower. Be warned. The soap is scented. Your sailor friends might notice.'

'I don't care.'

* *

The bathroom was a spacious, tiled room with a wet area in the corner, above which was mounted a large shower head. I stood under the hot shower, soaped all over with a generous cake of sweet-smelling soap, and suspended all thought. Afterwards, I towelled myself dry and looked in the full-length mirror. I saw the curly brown hair, blue eyes, wide shoulders, and sturdy build inherited from my Scottish–New Zealand father, and the regular features and slightly olive skin from my Spanish mother. My body carried scars acquired in strange places and at strange times. My nose was broken and slightly off-centre. I did not know then that I would acquire more scars before I left Paraguay. I got dressed and was in bare feet, with my trouser cuffs rolled up.

I thought about the last thirty-six hours. A sense of intimacy, subtle but present, had grown between me and this clever, attractive woman. In little more than a day.

We had dinner, chatted. I switched from orange juice to red wine. Sophia had drunk at least a bottle and a half, but the only clue to her state of sobriety was that she smiled a lot. I spotted a book on a lower shelf and took it down.

She said, 'Put it on the lectern.'

I had not noticed but there was a lectern in a corner where it received lots of natural light. The binding of the book was beautiful, as were the typeface and the design and illustrations. Before I could comment she said, 'That is *The Canterbury Tales*, written in Middle English by Geoffrey Chaucer between 1387 and 1400. That edition was published by William Morris' Kelmscott Press in 1896. Isn't it beautiful?'

'It's wonderful. So is your general knowledge. When I settle, I will collect books. I probably won't be able to afford this one, but you never know.'

Sophia said, 'Tell me more about New Zealand, and your hometown.'

I told her about European settlement starting in the mid-nineteen century, and about the indigenous people, Māori, Polynesians from the South Pacific, proud, fierce warriors, creative. The marae and canoes decorated with ornate and beautiful carvings, inlaid with polished paua shells. They often made war on each other, enslaving the defeated, and sometimes cannibalising them. How the settlers made war on Māori, on and off for twenty-five years, confiscating almost all their lands. About the settlement of Dunedin by Scotsmen and -women, most of them strict

Calvinists. The first ships of 1848. A city laid out in Scotland by people who did not know that the site was almost all hills. The gold rushes inland turned the city into the richest one in New Zealand and its financial capital. The population of New Zealand growing to a million by 1908, now about one and a half million in less than a hundred years, more than Paraguay after its four hundred years of European settlement and its dictatorships, revolutions, civil wars, and wars with its neighbours.

I continued, 'Our society has a rough edge, unfinished, still a frontier. But with wealth comes high culture. There is a collector of medieval manuscripts in Dunedin, Sir Alfred Hamish Reed. A writer and publisher and something of an eccentric, he walks all over New Zealand, and never accepts a lift from motorists. He intends to bequeath his collection to the city.'

Sophia said, 'Put the Chaucer back on the shelf, there is something I want to show you.'

I was putting the book back when I heard a zipper being pulled and the rustle of fabric. I turned to find Sophia naked, with her dress in a pile about her ankles. Small breasts, flat stomach, pale skin, and a small patch of dark pubic hair, trimmed short.

Chapter Three
A War of Maps and Postage Stamps.
20 January 1932

Is even Paraguay going to push us around? War should be an adventure for Bolivia. Let us go to the Chaco, not to conquer or die but to conquer.
 – Daniel Domingo Salamanca Urey, President of Bolivia. 1931

The conquest of the Chaco will be a mere matter of marching.
 – General Hans Kundt, C-in C of the Bolivian Army. 1929

An invitation to meet with the Director of the Geographic Institute arrived at my ship a few days after my day and night with Sophia. I left the ship early and walked into the city. The air was warm and moist and scented with orange blossom from the groves to the east. I walked the unnamed streets, past houses with no numbers, hidden behind pastel-coloured walls of chipped stucco.

The directions had been clear, and soon I found the black hardwood door set into a wall beside the brass plate of the Instituto Geográfico de la Nacional República del Paraguay.

The silent Indian maid who answered the door led me along a path through a lush tropical garden, and into a high-ceilinged atrium. She indicated where I should sit. A tall, thin man of about seventy, with a kindly face and white hair, appeared. Dressed in a white shirt, black bow tie, a tailcoat, and pinstriped trousers, he introduced himself as Luca, the Director of the Institute.

He smiled and said, 'So you are a serious young sailor who is interested in everything? Sophia spoke warmly of you. You are the first New Zealander either of us has met.'

I said, 'A healthy curiosity makes life worth living.'

'It does.'

The Director led the way down a corridor and into a long, high-ceilinged room. Cabinets of map drawers lined one wall, three long tables occupied the centre of the room, and on the other side were floor-to-ceiling doors, folded back and opening onto a patio.

'Tea? Earl Grey, with lemon?' the Director asked.

'Thank you.'

The Director went to a bell pull and without words or delay the maid appeared, bearing a tray with two bowls of tea.

We sat at a table on the patio, facing north-west with a view of the port, the wide Rio Paraguay, and a distant shore, barely visible in the haze.

'How much do you know of the República?'

'It is a long way from anywhere. It took my ship seven days to steam from the River Plate estuary, up the Rio Parana and the Rio Paraguay. The rivers have multiple channels, and the main channel probably shifts about. You would know all about that. The company could not afford a river pilot and there were sections of the rivers where we needed to sound the depth with lead and line. We had to anchor at night and watch the navigation lights of the regular traffic pass us.'

'Sophia told me a little of your history, personal that is, not your country's.' He went inside and came back with a large map, dated 1905. He spread it on the table in front of us.

'The first thing to understand is that Paraguay is landlocked. And so is our neighbour, Bolivia, the only other landlocked country in Latin America.'

'Yes.'

'The best way to explain Paraguay's situation is to think about the War of the 70. We have long borders with Bolivia to the west and north, Argentina to the south-west and south, and Brazil to the north and east.

'The details are complex, but the basics are easy enough to understand. In 1864 the dictator Francisco Solano López, President of Paraguay, declared war on Brazil and invaded the Brazilian province of Mato Grosso, then he marched across Argentina to support one side of a Civil War in Uruguay. His allies lost the war, and within a few months we were at war with the Triple Alliance of Brazil, Argentina, and Uruguay. It was madness, the Alliance was far stronger than we were, but it took until 1870 to defeat us. One of the reasons it took so long was that the only way for large bodies of men to enter Paraguay was by way of the river systems. The Brazilians built a fleet of ironclads to support the armies. Paraguay built fortresses on the Rio Parana and Rio Paraguay. Each fell after a long siege and bombardments from the ironclads and attacks from the land side. After the fall of each, our Army would retreat up the rivers to a new fortress. The war did not end until López, his mistress, an Irish whore called Eliza Lynch, and his remaining troops had been cornered in north-eastern Paraguay and López was dead. The population in 1864 was about 390 thousand to 450 thousand. By the end of the war, the population had fallen to between 141 thousand and 166 thousand. Precision is impossible but some things are certain, the population fell by well over fifty-five percent, perhaps as much as seventy percent. There were only twenty-eight thousand adult males left and there were ten women for every man. This had some unique sociological effects that still linger. Our women are very assertive.'

'I have noticed.'

The Director smiled. 'The population was slow to recover, it is still only about 980 thousand. It would be much larger but for the demographic effects of the losses in that terrible war. And López was a butcher. His

English technical experts had given notice, so López thanked them, paid them, and gutted those who had not had the wit to run when they had the chance. During his final retreat, he took the time to have family members whipped. He was court-martialling and executing loyal and efficient officers until the moment a Brazilian bayoneted him in a swamp.'

'Why didn't someone assassinate him?'

'Fear and hope. A dictator like López survives by instilling fear in everyone. They all hope they will survive and all know that even if they succeed in killing him, they will be executed by his praetorian guard, his bodyguards, before things settle down.'

'How is López regarded today?'

'He is despised by the Liberals, but the Colorados, the Conservatives, are trying to rehabilitate his memory. Now you know why our National Anthem is called "Republic or Death", but enough of López.

'There are two Paraguays — the Occidental and the Oriental. The River Paraguay runs due north for about eight hundred kilometres. East of the river, the Oriental, it is a hilly, green, fertile, and subtropical region. Most of the country's people live there, mainly in villages or on farms, and most of them live along the railway from Asunción to Encarnación. To the west of the Paraguay and north of the Pilcomayo, the Occidental, lies the Chaco Boreal, the northern part of the Gran Chaco, a vast alluvial plain extending to the foothills of the Andes about six hundred kilometres away. No one knows how many people live there, some Indians, some loggers, and ranchers. A community of Anabaptists, Mennonites. A few thousand people perhaps, no one knows for sure. The Paraguayan and Bolivian Armies are present in small numbers. Each country has established fortíns. Not really forts, usually just a collection of mud huts with thatched roofs and a few score soldiers. And a flagpole. The soldiers and the flags are symbols and statements. They are assertions of sovereignty. If war comes, they will be strongly fortified. Trench systems, barbed wire entanglements, bunkers, and machine-gun posts dug into the ground and roofed over with quebracho logs. The soldiers will go underground, just like on the Western Front in the Great War.'

He paused, then went on, 'The Chaco Boreal is about the size of the State of Michigan and bigger than England, Wales, and Scotland combined.'

'What is the Chaco like? Everyone I have spoken to about it says do not go there, and they talk about snakes and spiders.'

'Flat, featureless, hot and wet in the east, hot and dry in the west. From the west bank of the Rio Paraguay, there are inundations with small islands of palm trees. Further west the terrain is covered by thick forests of thorny trees, which are green in the rainy season and brown in the dry season. Further west still, there is a dusty, open semi-desert. In some months of the year, the east is almost as dry as the west. The climate is tropical, the hottest place in South America, but at times a strong wind from the south will drop the temperature from forty degrees Celsius to freezing in just a few hours. Most of the area has no drinkable water. It does have hundreds of species of flora and fauna, some of them unique, many of them dangerous. Few people visit it. This city was founded in 1537 and yet the Chaco is only now being explored.'

The Director fetched a sketch map, hesitated, and put the map back in its folder.

'There is a freshwater lake in an area where drinkable water is more valuable than gold. It is only a few hundred kilometres from here, but it was not discovered until March 1931, almost four hundred years after the founding of the city.'

I noted that the Director had been vague about the lake's precise location, suggesting that the location was strategically significant and that the fewer people who knew where it was, the better.

'We think that its existence is known only to us and the Indians. Perhaps the Bolivians have found it, perhaps not.'

'Where is the border with Bolivia?'

'Paraguay and Bolivia have been arguing about that since independence in the early 1800s.'

The Director fetched maps of Paraguay. On all of them, the area from the west bank of the Rio Paraguay to the eastern foothills of the Andes was marked 'Chaco Paraguayo'. One showed several provisional borders with dates from the nineteenth- and early-twentieth centuries. He explained that agreements had been reached several times. Each of those lines showed a border that had been negotiated but not ratified by one or both countries' legislatures.

'Currently, tensions are high. There have been numerous minor clashes since the late 1920s.' The Director opened a large leather-and-canvas bound scrapbook and pointed to a news clipping that read:

BOLIVIAN OUTRAGE. MURDER OF PARAGUAYAN OFFICER

Bolivian soldiers have murdered Second Lieutenant Rojas Silver in an unprovoked attack on a party of soldiers in the Paraguayan Chaco. We understand that a small party of our soldiers were peacefully conducting a survey when a large detachment of Bolivian soldiers, who had no right to be on Paraguayan soil, arrested them at gunpoint. The circumstances of the murder are not entirely clear, but Lieutenant Silver was either trying to escape, as was his duty, or he was murdered in cold blood. The news was carried by a soldier who managed to escape and reached one of our fortíns. The Government has registered a strong complaint through our embassy in La Paz and to the League of Nations in Geneva. The President has demanded the release of our prisoners, the payment of an indemnity and exemplary punishment of the Bolivian soldiers responsible.

– La Tribuna y Patria, Asunción. 28 February 1927

'The population of our country has become polarised; most believe the whole Chaco is ours and we should stop negotiating and go to war. The Government believes that if it shows weakness, it will be overthrown. There is no war and no peace.'

'What is there worth fighting about?'

'It's complicated. The Casado Company leases fifty thousand square kilometres of the Chaco and logs the quebracho trees. Other concerns lease blocks of land almost as expansive. The timber is processed to produce hardwood for building, and tannin for use in tanning leather. They also ranch cattle for hides and meat. There are other factors, too. The Bolivians have found oil in the foothills of the Andes. Perhaps the oil companies think there is oil in the disputed zone and are pressuring the governments concerned. We have Standard Oil on our side. The Bolivians have Royal Dutch Shell.

'There is a politico-strategic imperative for the Bolivians. Bolivia had a coastline on the Pacific Ocean, including the port city of Arica. All Bolivian trade flowed through the port until Bolivia and Peru were defeated by Chile in the War of the Pacific in 1879 to 1884, and Bolivia lost its entire Pacific coastline and the port. By a treaty with Chile, Bolivia has access to the port and a railway from Arica to La Paz, but the Chileans can cut this at any time they like. This makes the Bolivians nervous. They have also lost territory to Peru, Brazil, and Argentina. If Bolivia acquires the whole Chaco region, they can establish a port across the river from here and have access to the South Atlantic, as we do. It also means that our capital will be within artillery range of a nation that believes that it has good cause to hate us.

'Bolivia sees Paraguay's land grants to the Casado Company and similar concerns, and to the Mennonites in the Chaco, as aggressive and disrespectful. Paraguay feels the same way about Bolivia extending its line of outposts further and further east using the same tactics. The Bolivians have tried to have the Mennonites accept Bolivian titles to the land. All the settlers want is to be left alone. The pride of both nations is at stake. The two nations are waging a War of the Postage Stamps.'

I must have looked puzzled. The Director fetched an album, placed it on the table and opened it to show four stamps. Each of the stamps showed a map of the Chaco. The three Paraguayan stamps showed the Paraguayan border in the western part of the Chaco, close to the eastern foothills of the Andes. The Bolivian stamp showed the Bolivian border on the Rio Paraguay.

He said, 'A Bolivian border on the Paraguay River is unacceptable to Paraguay. Paraguay lost territory to Brazil and Argentina after the War of the 70 and will not tolerate losing anymore. Also, Bolivia is more populous and richer in resources than Paraguay. If the Bolivians controlled the west bank of the river, they could invade Eastern Paraguay any time they wished. Paraguay wants the Chaco as a buffer zone. Bolivia has three times our population plus mineral resources, mainly tin, that we do not have. But the price of tin is low. And Bolivia has been called the beggar on the golden throne, the money never filters down to the poor, the bulk of the population. One hundred Bolivian families are very rich, and there is a growing middle class. The rest are poor, as poor as a large majority of my countrymen and -women. Bolivia should be strong and stable but is not and never has been. Since 1905, serious exploration of the Chaco has been conducted, and military outposts have been established by both Bolivia and Paraguay. The line of Bolivian outposts is now about two hundred kilometres from the river.'

The Director produced a large, multi-coloured map. 'This is a draft of the map the General has been working on. He has been exploring the Chaco since 1924 and is also an ethnographer, who has learned much about the tribes of Indians, their customs and way of life, and what territory each group considers to be their home. This map shows the regions occupied by each tribe. In less than ten years, the General has learned more about the Indians and the geography of the Chaco than all the explorers since the days of the conquistadors.'

'The General?'

'Juan Belaieff, a Russian, a White Russian, who is becoming more Paraguayan than the Paraguayans. You should meet him.'

It was after midday, the air hot and damp. The Director made his excuses and walked me through the garden to the door in the wall. He said, 'I will arrange an invitation to dinner at the General's house.'

I walked the streets towards the streetcar line. It was siesta time, and the streets were almost empty, heat shimmering off them, the houses quiet and shuttered, as if nothing had moved since I passed them that morning.

So, there was almost a war! There might be a real war. The Director had been passionate and proud of his forebears and their struggle against the Triple Alliance. But had Paraguay forgotten what war meant? Clearly, a compromise was the only bloodless way out. Passions were high and neither side had the emotional ability to do this.

* *

I was twelve when war broke out in 1914. New Zealand immediately declared war on Germany and later, Turkey and Austria-Hungary, and sent an expeditionary force to the Middle East. New Zealand lost almost three thousand dead at Gallipoli in 1915, and thousands more in France and Flanders. I went to high school assuming that I would go off to war as soon as I was finished. Almost every boy did. We looked forward to it or said we did. I was not so sure as I had volunteered to help care for wounded soldiers, many of them broken in body or mind, or both. My favourite patient was Hulme, who talked about the gardens he would have created had not the violence of the enemy taken his right arm at the shoulder.

For three weeks every year, we trained in the Army Cadet Corps in khaki serge uniforms, hobnail boots, puttees and caps, marching and saluting. Sometimes we did bayonet drill, stabbing straw men while shouting at the top of our voices 'in, out, on guard'. On the last two days of each training period, we went to the rifle range and shot with the standard infantry rifle and came home with shoulders bruised purple by the recoil. The senior cadets trained with the water-cooled Vickers machine gun. Six hundred rounds a minute for as long as the ammunition lasted.

In mid-1918, it seemed likely that the war would last into 1919 or even 1920, but the end came suddenly and unexpectedly.

I remembered the day the news of the armistice arrived. The armistice went into effect at eleven in the morning on 11 November 1918. It was already the twelfth in New Zealand. The Rector of my high school called a special assembly. The Great Hall was full of boys, aged thirteen to seventeen, in the grey school uniform. The Rector spoke for an hour, his message triumphalist. The dead were the Glorious Dead. Belgium had been liberated, the ideals of freedom and democracy had been vindicated. The Great War for Freedom had been won, at great cost, but the result was worth the blood and suffering. The dastardly Hun had been cowed. The Kaiser had abdicated and gone into exile in the Netherlands. The Allies should arrest him and hang him as a war criminal. Revolutionaries controlled the ports and the streets of Germany's cities.

He told the boys that the school had commissioned a volume, a folio, three-quarter bound in calfskin, in which calligraphers would inscribe the names of all former pupils who had died in the war. It would be finished on the first anniversary of the armistice. The names would be read out at an assembly each morning until every dead old boy had been mentioned. From then on, a page of the book would be read out by the head prefect at the special assembly on the morning of each Friday. In perpetuity.

On the afternoon of the day the news reached New Zealand, we had a general science class with Mr Aspinall, a man of few words, who could reduce complex concepts to easily understood language. He did not teach science during the period. Instead, he read out loud from Tolstoy's *War and Peace*, with its central event Napoleon's Russian Campaign of 1812. He told us that Tolstoy had been an officer in the Imperial Russian Army. His service had included colonial wars in the Caucasus and the Siege of Sevastopol during the Crimean War of 1853 to 1856. The novelist knew war.

I remembered the passage: a character hears of the peace and realises that he will not die, he would live, and it was wonderful.

The class became a seminar on what the boys were going to do, now that they would not be going off to the war. Another quote from the novel was read out. I remember it word for word: *I simply want to live; to cause no evil to anyone but myself.*

One boy wanted to be an engine driver, another an accountant; the boy with the tousled red hair was going to be an artist. On my last visit to Dunedin, I had attended an exhibition by the red-headed boy who was now a man and painting images in black and shades of grey, striking images that were, somehow, representative of the darkness in the souls of some of our countrymen.

One of the boys was going to England. I had heard that he had been commissioned into the Royal Marines, sent to North Russia to fight the Bolsheviks, and received fatal wounds in a skirmish that would be forgotten by history. He had lingered for two weeks and died the day before his nineteenth birthday.

My older brother had gone off to the war, trained as a pilot and flown Sopwith Triplanes and Camels with the Royal Naval Air Service and the Royal Air Force on the Western Front. He went on to fly in South Russia in 1919, against the Reds in the Russian Civil War. The three German and two Red Army aeroplanes he shot down would put him in the history books as an ace. Returning home unscathed, his war record was something he could dine out on for the rest of his life. Had I missed something by being too young to go? I faced seventy years of explaining that 'Yes, my brother is the flying ace and, no, I was too young to serve'.

The Irish poet William Butler Yeats had some insight. I remembered part of one of his poems, 'An Irish Airman Foresees His Death', written in the middle of the Great War.

> *Nor law, nor duty bade me fight,*
> *Nor public men, nor cheering crowds,*
> *A lonely impulse of delight*
> *Drove to this tumult in the clouds.*

A beautiful piece of writing, but Yeats had never sat in a burning aeroplane, at 5,000 metres, without a parachute, and only two options: burning alive or jumping.

I was bound for a solicitor's office and worked as a law clerk in dark, dusty rooms of offices where secrets might be kept. Several afternoons a week I went to the law faculty of the university for lectures and worked toward a Bachelor of Laws degree.

I reached the line and boarded a streetcar back to the centre of Asunción. Soon I was riding through streets lined with office buildings, occupied by importers, exporters, insurance companies, newspapers, lawyers, and doctors, framed by the many telephone wires strung from poles, along and across the streets.

I bought the day's newspapers, walked to the Café Indio, ordered coffee, and settled down to read and write. I opened my journal and wrote about the day. The city came to life around me, people returning to work.

Chapter Four
A General. 23 January 1932

A few days after my visit to the Institute, I found myself at the home of Juan Belaieff.

The dinner table was outside in the central courtyard. Its dark mahogany surface was covered in a white damask tablecloth and set for twenty people. The General was a short, slim man of about fifty-five with a completely bald, egg-shaped head, a neat Vandyke beard, and a friendly expression. He sat at the head of the table. The evening had started with drinks in a large living room with a high ceiling, decorated with native art.

The General had circulated, introducing me to a few of the other guests, half of whom were military officers in uniform. I met officers from the infantry, cavalry, and artillery, and two from the air service, one of them a White Russian named Vladimir Nesterov. The General was the best kind of host, always ready to listen and to laugh at his guests' jokes. He treated everyone as if they were a guest of honour.

I owned no clothes fit for such an affair but had taken the trouble to wash my best trousers and press them under my mattress, sponge down my only jacket and my only tie, and polish my shoes. At least my host would see that I had tried to dress appropriately.

After an hour or so of drinking and talking, when the party was relaxed and a little rowdy, we went into dinner. There were two empty seats, one on each side at the head of the table. The dishes were served by maids in starched, black-and-white uniforms, all of whom appeared short, dark-skinned, round in the face, impassive, and competent.

Sophia was there. She had arrived with a young man in uniform, displaying the insignia of the artillery. She introduced him. 'Travis, meet Alfredo Stroessner Matiauda.' Stroessner was a slim, serious-looking young man, about twenty years of age. We exchanged courtesies.

We had been at the table for about half an hour when a couple arrived, and everyone stood to acknowledge them. The couple joined us, and the party continued.

The other aviator, an Argentinian called Patricio McMahon, nudged me and whispered, 'That's the President, José Patricio Guggiari Corniglione, and Madam Guggiari. You will be introduced later. The man sitting to the President's right is Arturo Bray, an up-and-coming Army officer.'

Bray was a serious-looking man of about thirty-five. I said, 'Bray looks as if he does not laugh often.'

'He was in the British Army in the Great War, wounded in France on the Western Front. He returned healed in body but not in mind. He has lost his facility for pleasure. It is said he has not smiled in fifteen years.'

I looked at Bray. *It would be an unpleasant experience getting on the wrong side of him*, I thought, not knowing that I would soon find out.

Vladimir Nesterov had discovered I was a pilot and since pilots have an infinite capacity for discourse on flying, I was soon deep in conversation with him. He had learned to fly just before the Bolshevik Revolution of October 1917. Russia had left the Great War against Germany and Austria-Hungary before he had a chance to fly in combat. When the Civil War between the Reds and Whites broke out, he had joined General Denikin, who led the White or anti-Bolshevik forces in South Russia.

He described conditions in the area during the Civil War. 'Politics and operations were unbelievably complicated, and defeat often meant torture and execution, or if the prisoner was lucky, summary execution. A friend of mine was far more fortunate. He was shot down close to a column of soldiers whom he had been strafing and was captured. He was wearing a worn flying suit over an oil-stained set of mechanic's overalls. His face was deeply tanned, his hands were hard from much labouring in the fields. This was on his estate, with his fifty peasant labourers. There was no money in his pockets, he was not wearing a wristwatch, and there was no evidence that he was an officer. He passed himself off as a proletarian who had been forced to fly for the counter-revolutionaries. It helped that he read widely and was familiar with the works of Marx, Engels, and Lenin. They believed him. After a few weeks he was released in a quiet sector so he could return to his unit to spread revolution.'

I replied, 'A happy story in a war conspicuously short of happy stories?'

'Yes indeed. As I was saying, things were complicated. Units often changed sides, some of them more than once. There were interventions by the British in North and South Russia, and in the Baltic. The French in South Russia briefly fought alongside White Forces, and there were Japanese and Americans in Siberia. Anyway, I instructed airmen, organised the maintenance group, and flew a few sorties. I almost shot down a Red Fokker D.VII.' He paused, smiled and added, 'Well, I shot at it.'

'My brother was in South Russia in 1919, with the Royal Air Force,' I said, and told him about my brother's service in the region.

He replied, 'I don't remember him. Perhaps our paths did not cross. It was all quite traumatic for me. I remember some things vividly, others not at all.'

Nesterov had gone from cheerful to solemn as White Russians usually did when talking about the wars that cost them their country. He went on, 'By 1920, General Wrangel was leading us. On 14 November 1920, we evacuated our base in Crimea, taking a hundred and forty-five thousand civilians, and many soldiers and sailors, with us. General Belaieff and I were suddenly officers without an army and men without a homeland. But that was not quite the end of Imperial Russia. The Black Sea Fleet sailed with us. I will never forget that day.'

It was clearly memorable because he went on with some precise statistics.

'I even remember the ships, the battleships *General Alekseyev* and *Georgii Pobedonosets* ...'

He continued naming every ship in the fleet, and then said, 'The French gave the Black Sea Fleet asylum, and from 1921, it remained anchored at Bizerte in Tunisia. Every morning, the ships raised the naval ensign of Imperial Russia until one day in 1924. Imagine that! The Czar, Czarina, and their children had been murdered in June 1918, but their flag flew for another six years! This practice only ended when the French recognised Soviet Russia. The White Naval officers and men dispersed. The Soviets inspected the fleet but found it fit only for scrap.'

'Why did the Whites lose the Civil War?'

'The Reds stood for something, something clear and easy to understand, but the Whites were made up of a multitude of factions and never agreed what they stood for. The Reds were ruthless all the time; the Whites were inconsistent and often appeared weak. The peoples of Imperial Russia feared the return of despotism. Eventually, the people wanted peace at any price. They had no idea how ghastly the rule of Lenin and his followers would be. Did you know that there is a famine in Ukraine? We think that at least a million people have died. It is man-made, deliberate, so awful that it has a name, the Holodomor.'

'It does not seem to have appeared in the newspapers.'

'The Soviets have rigid censorship; little news gets out and their fellow travellers denounce the rumours of disaster as counter-revolutionary lies. The Soviets have a name for these people: useful idiots.'

'How do you come to be in Paraguay?'

'The General arrived in 1924 and made a home here and persuaded the Government to hire other émigré officers, including me.'

'What does the General do?'

'He heads the engineering department at the Military School and has made journeys into the Chaco. More than a dozen.' He went on confirming what the Director had told me. 'And he started preparing a dictionary of the language of the most interesting tribe, the Maká, I think. He knows more about the Chaco Boreal than anyone else alive. By the way, when a Paraguayan or a Bolivian talks about the Gran Chaco or Chaco, they mean the Chaco Boreal.'

'I have seen the map.'

The conversation returned to aviation. He said, 'Would you like to go flying?'

'Yes, I would, very much so.'

'I will arrange it. If I left a message with Sophia, would it get to you?' *Nothing is a secret here, just like at home! Both countries with cities that are more like villages, where everyone knows everyone else's business.* I told him that the message would reach me.

I had used the bathroom and I was on my way back to the courtyard when I took a wrong turn and walked into the kitchen. I heard a muffled scream and saw a young Indian girl looking distressed and smoothing down her dress. A young man in uniform stepped away from her. It was Sophia's escort, Alfredo Stroessner. He glanced at me and calmly walked past me to the door.

A guest arrived in the uniform of a Lieutenant-Colonel of Infantry. I was introduced by Nesterov. 'José Félix Estigarribia Insaurralde. This is Connor Travis. His family could not afford more than two names.'

The shortness of my name had become something I was teased about. We shook hands. Estigarribia was a man of about forty-five, below medium height, with shiny black hair brushed straight back, and a face that suggested intelligence, intensity, and a sense of humour.

One of my new friends at the party was known as a well-informed gossip. Later in the evening, he said, 'Estigarribia is only a Lieutenant-Colonel, but he is the coming man.'

Another officer, a Major of Infantry arrived, and I was introduced to him. This time the shortness of my name was not mentioned. The officer was Rafael Franco, who gave the impression of being a serious man with, unusual for a serious man, a sense of humour. He went on to talk to Arturo Bray, who just looked serious.

My friend said, 'Have you heard about the massacre at the Presidential Palace? Late last year?'

'Yes, a little.'

'Franco is quite the revolutionary. It is rumoured that he tried to organise a coup in February last year, but nothing came of it. In late October, he gave incendiary speeches to gatherings of students from the high schools and the university. Along the lines that not enough was being done to prepare for war with Bolivia. A mob went to the Palace, could not find the President, and went looking for him. Stones were thrown, windows broken, that kind of thing. They were roughly handled by the police. Next day the mob returned to the Palace and attempted to break in. Bray commanded a detachment of soldiers armed with rifles and a machine gun. The facts are disputed, but it is certain that the soldiers opened fire, killing at least twelve students, and wounding many more. The President stepped down in favour of the Vice-President, was acquitted at the impeachment trial, and resumed his Presidency. A unique set of events.'

The host tapped a crystal glass to get our attention and proposed a lengthy and ornate toast to the President and his lady. The President toasted the General. A protracted round of toasts ensued. Much champagne was drunk. The women retired and the men went out to the patio, settled into wicker chairs, and were offered cognac and coarse black cigars. I lit mine and unwisely inhaled deeply, only to have a coughing fit.

The General smiled. 'They are an acquired preference.'

I nodded and drank deeply of the cognac, finding that it removed much of the foul taste.

The guests included a German farmer, a novelist, and a salesman for the German arms manufacturer Krupp. Somehow, I learned that the farmer had been a pilot, so I chatted with him. I told him that I had wanted to be a pilot since I was about twelve years old.

'In early 1914, at Dunedin, I watched an aviator called Will Scotland make the first flight in the city. We applauded as he climbed into the cockpit, wearing a tall leather crash helmet. The machine was a Caudron biplane with the engine at the front and the pilot sitting behind in a nacelle the size of a large bathtub. The tail was mounted on booms, and the booms and the wings braced with numerous wires. He took off, and as he banked and turned between the crowd and the sun, the structure showed clearly through the turquoise-blue doped fabric covering. By the time Scotland made a final graceful turn and glided in to land, I had fallen in love with the idea of flying. I persuaded my father to subscribe to the British aviation weeklies *Flight* and *The Aeroplane,* and we both read every issue cover to cover.'

The German's name was Kurt Buckler, and his story was more interesting than mine. He had been an infantry officer at the front in France and Flanders and was twice wounded. He assumed war flying was no more dangerous than the combat he had experienced, and he obtained a transfer to the air service, learned to fly, and arrived at his fighter squadron the evening before the armistice took effect. After the war, he joined Kampfgeschwader Sachsenberg, a Freikorps aviation unit supporting General Rüdiger von der Goltz's Iron Division, fighting Bolsheviks in the Baltic States.

Buckler said, 'If someone tells you he understands the politics of the Baltic States after the war, don't believe him — no one does. I was there and I don't pretend to.'

Before he could elaborate, the party started to break up. We agreed to meet and talk flying, and he gave me his telephone number.

I wondered if there were any other country where a stranger, and only a seaman, would be invited to dinner with so many interesting people, including a general and a president.

Around two in the morning, Sophia circulated, inviting all of us for a nightcap at her place. Outside were large shiny cars with chauffeurs waiting for the bigwigs. A car was parked in front of ours and a familiar figure was standing by it. The man I had seen twice before, in cafés, not doing very much of anything. There was nothing suspicious in him being here as a chauffeur, but I felt a tickle of anxiety. Was I being watched?

At least ten of us jammed ourselves into someone's car. Our host had provided each of us with a traveller: a glass of some lethal mixture of fruit juice and vodka. I gossiped with someone I could hear but not see, and we soon pulled up outside Sophia's apartment.

Two horses were hitched to a railing outside. One was saddled and the other had packs draped over it. I asked Sophia, 'One of your guests?'

'Yes.'

'He looks as though he is about to ride off somewhere.'

She laughed, and said, 'He is.'

We went upstairs and she introduced me to the horseman. 'Our Argentinian friend, Aimé Félix Tschiffely, from Buenos Aires.'

I asked him, 'How far are you going?'

He laughed. 'Oh, pretty far.'

He smiled and started talking about his horses. I have avoided horses wherever possible, but pretended to be interested, and we chatted about how he had selected his, what breed they were, and why that breed was best suited for the journey. He told me that their names were Gato and Mancha and that each had a distinct personality. They were so tame he rarely tied them up. I drifted away and listened to a group discussing Shakespeare. One of the men was reciting King Henry's speech before Agincourt, from *Henry V*, accurately and in perfect English. A woman was talking in German about the place of chess in nineteenth-century fiction. She had written books and learned papers about the subject.

I found myself next to a university professor. He said, 'Sophia tells me you are interested in our history?'

'I am.'

'How interested?'

'Enough to listen to whatever you have to tell me.'

'I'll get some lubrication before I start. A drink for you?' he asked.

'Yes.'

Soon we both had drinks in our hands.

'Our constitution is a noble document and guarantees the most important freedoms and rights, but it is difficult to apply,' he said. 'We are, should be, a democracy, and live under a rule of law, with justice for all, but we have always been chronically politically unstable, from the earliest days of independence from Spain. The wars of independence in Hispanic America during the early nineteenth century were bloody and long. Almost everywhere but Paraguay. Argentina attempted to attach us as a province, but we defeated them so often they gave up. We gained our independence around 1811. With a minimum of violence. We were remote. We had no precious metals or other sources of wealth, a few cattle, quebracho trees, and oranges, not much else. I think Spain thought it was not worth their while to oppose the independence movement. They may have forgotten we existed.'

He took a sip of his drink, and continued, 'From 1814 to 1870, there were three dictatorships. First, Dr José Gaspar Rodríguez de Francia y Velasco, El Supremo, from 1814 to his death in 1840. El Supremo cut this country off from the outside world, made Paraguay into an inland Japan. Then the López dynasty. Carlos Antonio López Ynsfrán from 1844 to 1862, and his son, Francisco Solano López Carrillo, from 1862 to 1870. Paraguay was opened up to the outside world while the Lópezes were in power. We lost a war in 1870 …'

I broke in. 'The War of the 70?'

'You have heard of this war and its consequences?'

'I have.'

'We lost and were occupied for five or six years. Since the mid-1870s, we have had at least thirty presidents. Only one of them served out his term. You have seen the Central Police Station?'

'Yes.'

'Notice anything about the building?'

'Damage. Repaired but imperfectly. An earthquake?'

'Artillery and machine guns and small arms. In a revolution, the Central Police Station is one of the buildings that must be controlled and ours has been fought over more than once.'

'How often?'

'In most of our troubled times. In 1904, the Liberals overthrew the Colorado Party. In 1908, there was fighting between factions within the Liberal Party Government. Again in 1911 to 1912. Then there was the Civil War of 1922 to 1923, when thousands died. We have lost count of the coups and uprisings and civil wars. There are also slightly more subtle events, premature changes of government brought about by negotiation and ill-disguised threats. We are used to it. A few idealists struggle against the instability.' He looked serious for a moment, then continued, 'A visitor joked that revolutions are our national sport, but then he had not seen and smelt the blood and bodies in the street, or the firing squads at work.'

I found myself next to Sophia. 'That's a handsome young man you are with,' I said.

'Yes, he is,' she replied. 'And he has a great future.'

'How so?' I asked. But before she could answer, a couple of garrulous partygoers highjacked her.

After a time, the party spilt out into the street to farewell the rider. They sang a ragged version of the Argentine national anthem. He bowed from the saddle, tipped his hat, and rode off to three rousing cheers.

I turned to Sophia. 'Where is he going?'

'New York.'

'New York, riding a horse?'

'He is.'

And he was. Years later, I found a report in an old Argentinian newspaper. The yellowed cutting is in front of me as I write. The journey took 3 years and 149 days, through 20 countries, over mountain passes up to 5,000 metres high, in temperatures ranging from minus 18 degrees to plus 56 degrees Celsius. I took that high altitude and the high temperature with a grain of salt, but the journey was remarkable, a twentieth-century odyssey. On his return, he put his horses out to pasture, and when they died, he had them stuffed and gave them to a museum, where they gather dust to this day.

We went back upstairs. I could not get over the fact that a man was going to ride to New York, and said so to Sophia, who replied, 'If you think that is strangely impressive, I will introduce you to Isidoro Larregui, the Basque of the Wheelbarrow, next time he is in town. Isidoro is another Argentinian, from Comandante Luis Piedrabuena, a town about two thousand kilometres from the capital. One day he woke up and decided he would push his wheelbarrow to Buenos Aires. It took him more than a year.'

'Why?'

She shrugged. 'It must have seemed like a good idea at the time. And he did not stop there, he made several journeys, at least ten thousand kilometres in total.'

Years later, I asked my assistant to look him up, and she told me that no one knows exactly how many kilometres he pushed that wheelbarrow, except that it was more than twenty thousand, and that his wheelbarrow is in the same museum that houses Gato and Mancha.

I said to Sophia, 'Have I got this right — Franco incited the students to attack the Presidential Palace; Bray ordered his soldiers to fire on the students, killing twelve of them and wounding many more; President Guggiari asked for an impeachment trial and turned the Presidency over to the Vice-President?'

Sophia replied, 'That is correct.'

I thought for a moment, then said, 'And Guggiari was acquitted, is President again, and he and Bray and Franco can attend the same party without any sign of discomfort from them or any of the other guests?'

Sophia gave me one of her radiant smiles and said, 'That's right, only in Paraguay.'

The party wound down. Sophia came over. 'Would you like to stay the night?'

'Yes, but I thought you were with young Stroessner?'

She smiled. 'Oh, he has gone home, or for a walk. I am too old for him. Much too old. He is a solitary sort of young man.'

Chapter Five
An Airfield. 26 January 1932

At 6.30 am I set off for the airfield by streetcar and bicycle. A pampero had passed through just before dawn, scrubbing the air of its heat and moisture and leaving the scented air warm and mellifluous.

Nesterov had been as good as his word, I was responding to an invitation to fly with him that had arrived a few days after the party.

The guards at the gate raised the striped barrier and waved me through with smiles. There was no fence. They must have thought that anyone who chose to enter by the gate was entitled to.

Nesterov was waiting in front of the hangars, beside a Morane-Saulnier MS. 129, an elegant but old two-seat trainer with a swept-back parasol wing, braced with a king post and wires. The wheels were chocked, and a mechanic was waiting to swing the propeller. We agreed that Nesterov should talk me through a preflight inspection, so we worked our way around the aeroplane in an anticlockwise direction, checking fuel and oil and the condition of all vital components, including the many bracing wires, wires connecting the control surfaces to the stick and rudder, and the condition of the doped fabric, which covered most of the airframe.

Every aeroplane has a distinct personality, and I was experienced enough to make a good guess at what this new type might have to offer. It was a standard type of trainer, and I guessed that its handling would be straightforward, but engine management might be a challenge. Nowadays craft of this type are only seen in museums and air displays. It was a five-cylinder, air-cooled rotary of about eighty horsepower. The cylinders were arranged in a star shape. This type of engine took some finesse and skill to handle, as the crankshaft was bolted to the engine bearers and the cylinders and propeller were bolted together and rotated as one unit. This meant that there were strong gyroscopic forces that had to be compensated for in flight. The engine had no throttle, and power could be varied only a little by adjusting the fuel–air mixture. Too lean and it stopped, too rich and it stopped. For taxiing or low-speed flight, or approaching to land, the trick was to adjust the mixture so that the engine was producing less than full power, and to adjust revs by switching the magneto off and on. A button on the top of the stick, called the blip switch, allowed the pilot to do this. Holding the button down cut the ignition and the revs reduced. If the switch was held down too long, the engine would not pick up. There was also a risk that unburnt fuel could gather in the cowling, and if too much was swirling around, it might ignite when the switch was released. Accident rates in training in the Great War were enormous and often caused by the mishandling of rotary engines. For every pilot killed or seriously injured by the enemy, there was one who suffered the same fate in training or non-operational flying. My first three hundred hours flying was in an Avro with a rotary engine, and some of the types I flew in China were powered with rotaries, so I would not embarrass myself.

Nesterov helped me on with my overalls and adjusted the straps of an Italian-made parachute so that it fitted comfortably. The aeroplane was flown from the rear seat and the instructor sat in front with a set of dual controls. We had agreed on a flight plan and simple hand signals, and there was a rear-view mirror on the centre section of the wing that allowed the instructor to see the pupil. My helmet had a communication system somewhat like a stethoscope. Nesterov could shout down a mouthpiece, his words being conducted through tubes to rubber cups set into the earpieces of my soft leather flying helmet. He would be shouting technical words in heavily accented Spanish to someone whose first language was

English, over the noise of the slipstream and the engine. So I doubted I would understand much.

Soon I was strapped in the open cockpit. With the ignition switch off, the mechanic pulled the propeller through, one cylinder at a time, squirting raw petrol into each inlet valve. He shouted 'Contact'. I switched the magneto on, said 'Contact', and gave a thumbs up. With both hands on the propeller, he put all his weight into pulling the propeller down half a turn, and the engine caught and ran with a gust of castor oil smoke. I adjusted the air and petrol for slow running and the engine ran with an uneven crackle. I held down and released the blip switch every few seconds, keeping the revs down, the engine making a distinctive blipping sound each time.

The scent of castor oil, the sound, the sweet nostalgia of never-to-be-forgotten flights.

The simple instruments indicated that all was well with the engine. I signalled two of the mechanics to lie across the rear fuselage, held the stick hard back, and increased to full power, checking the tachometer and oil pressure and temperature, raising a cloud of dust behind. Adjusting the mixture, I signalled for the chocks to be pulled away and taxied toward the corner of the airfield using the rudder to swing the nose from side to side, allowing me to see ahead, past the long nose.

The windsock hung limp, so I chose to take off parallel to the hangars, workshops, and offices. I lined up, checking the rudder, elevators and ailerons for full and free movement and carefully adjusted the air and petrol levers. I felt and heard the engine smooth out and the slipstream stiffen the rudder and elevator control. Holding the stick forward brought the tail up and I could see directly ahead. The machine became buoyant, and it lifted and began to climb as I made a gentle turn to the north-east. I had a cloth looped through the top button of my overalls and from time to time I wiped a thin film of castor oil from my goggles.

As the aeroplane climbed, I essayed a few gentle turns to the left and right, levelling out at 900 metres. I did a steep turn to the left through 360 degrees, reversed the turn, and did the same to the right. Nesterov signalled that I should do a two-turn spin to the left and then one to the right. I reduced power and held the stick back to maintain height, blipping the mag switch, and keeping straight with reference to a feature on the ground. As we approached the stall, I could feel the turbulent airflow buffeting the tail and pulled the stick hard back and applied full left rudder and full right aileron. The nose dropped suddenly, and the aircraft started to rotate rapidly to the left in a steep nose-down attitude. After a turn and a half, I applied full right rudder, centred the stick and eased it forward until the aeroplane stopped rotating. I levelled the wings, pulled the nose up above the horizon, increasing power and climbing until we had recovered the lost height. I repeated the manoeuvre to the right and then Nesterov signalled that he had control.

The machine dived to gain speed for a loop and then soared up, up and over the top smoothly, and gracefully recovered, regaining the lost height and levelling out. I took control and repeated the manoeuvre. Nesterov demonstrated a stall turn, in which the Morane climbed vertically and, just before it stalled, he applied full right rudder and left aileron and the aircraft cartwheeled into a vertical dive. I took over and did a stall-turn to the right and one to the left and then it was time to return to the airfield.

We flew over the airfield and found there was no wind and no other traffic. Reducing the power and blipping the engine, I did a shallow descending turn to the right. I straightened out at about a hundred metres, aiming at a point well beyond the boundary. I sideslipped to steepen the glide and with one smooth motion, yawed the Morane straight with the rudder, levelled the wings with the ailerons and eased the stick back until the wheels and tail skid touched in a perfect three-pointer.

I taxied in, blipping the ignition switch to keep the speed down.

A mechanic held back the port wing as I applied full left rudder and gave a burst of power to help swing the aircraft around. Nesterov signalled for me to leave the engine running. He climbed out of the front cockpit, reached in to unscrew his control stick, stowed it in a pocket in the side of the cockpit, and buckled his seatbelt clear of the controls. He leant into my cockpit and shouted, 'Do three circuits solo.'

I did the circuits, making passable three-pointers on each landing and taxied back to the hangars.

Back at the hangar, I divested myself of parachute, overalls, helmet, and goggles. I chatted with Nesterov about the flight. 'Weren't you afraid I would prang your aeroplane, or fly off?'

He smiled and said, 'Your flying is fine, and you only had twenty-five minutes of fuel. You would not have got far.'

Morane Saulnier MS. 129. No. 4. V. Nesterov. Self. 50 minutes.

Morane Saulnier MS. 129. No. 4. Self. Circuits x 3. 15 minutes.

– Connor Travis, Pilot's Logbook. 26 January 1932

I felt the familiar satisfaction, the one I felt after almost every flight, of having been separated from earth-bound concerns and having moved freely in three dimensions, something that only pilots can experience. I had flown a new type, in a new place, made a new friend, and knew that I had done well.

In my life down to this time, the prime motivator was hedonism. Flying — part challenge, part danger — was one of the pleasures that drove my life choices. These flights in Paraguay were not as dangerous as those in China, Manchuria, or Afghanistan, but enough to heighten the senses, enough to make my day.

Before I left, I was introduced to a pilot who was also head of the maintenance group, a serious officer called Fernando de San Martin who talked to Nesterov, saying, 'What, you have let a foreigner loose on one of our deadly war machines?'

The aeroplane would not have been out of place on a training airfield in the Great War and carried no weapons, so his comments were clearly intended to be humorous. We chatted for a while.

I wanted to talk to Sophia and describe to her how wonderful the sensations of flight had been. San Martin said I could use the phone in his office, and I rang Sophia and was invited around. We agreed on seven that evening.

Chapter Six
The Military School. 27 January 1932

GEORGE V, by the Grace of God of Great Britain, Ireland, and the British dominions beyond the sea, King, Defender of the Faith, Emperor of India, &. To our Trusty and well-beloved Connor Travis, Greetings: WE, reposing especial Trust and Confidence in your loyalty, courage, and good Conduct, do by these Presents Constitute and Appoint you to be an Officer in our Royal Air Force …
– Connor Travis, RAF Commission Scroll. 1 November 1925

Total flight time as pilot in command: 2,314 hours 45 minutes. Assessment. As pilot: Exceptional. As navigator: Exceptional.
– Connor Travis, RAF Pilot's Logbook. 21 January 1930

Most of my worldly possessions can be contained in two water- and insect-proof trunks. Three white cotton shirts. Two pairs of black trousers (wool). Black jacket (corduroy). One set of dungarees (well worn). One black linen suit. One wool knit tie (red). Three sets of underwear. Three pairs of wool socks. A pair of brown leather brogues (well worn). One pair of brown leather hobnail boots (well worn). Passport and personal papers. Joseph Conrad, Nostromo, The Secret Agent *(Spanish editions, Madrid, 1928). Manuel Cervantes,* Don Quixote *(Spanish Edition, Madrid, 1885).* English–Spanish & Spanish–English Dictionary. *Assorted technical books.* Leica II *camera and 20 rolls of 35 mm film. Eight exposed. Spencer, Browning & Co. sextant. .455-calibre Webley revolver, cleaning kit and 50 rounds. Bayonet and sheath. Whetstone. Browning automatic rifle, Model of 1918 & cleaning kit & 3 magazines & 150 rounds of 30.06 ammunition. 6 sealed decks of cards. 12 British pounds, 27 US Dollars, 30 gold half-sovereigns. Journal, pen & ink, sketchbook, coloured pencils, charcoal sticks. Rucksack.*

– Connor Travis, Journal. 8 January 1932

Arturo Bray had been reading the parchment commission scroll out loud. He stopped reading, put the scroll down and fixed me with his cold gaze. 'Why is an officer in the Royal Air Force pretending to be a seaman on a tramp steamer? Why are you in Paraguay? Are you a spy?'

Less than twenty-four hours ago, I was revelling in the familiar sensations of flight and now I was being examined by what looked suspiciously like a tribunal. Although, I could only guess what it was, what it wanted, and what powers it had.

I had been sitting in my favourite café when a large black car had pulled up, and two men dressed in identical black suits, white shirts, and black ties, had got out and politely asked me to accompany them. One of them was the man I had seen several times in cafés and once outside the General's house. He had been watching me. The most sinister aspect of this was that he had made no effort at concealment. I felt a small shot of ice water to my heart. I thought, *Pyragues, the secret police*. Sophia had told me about them. The literal meaning of the word is 'the hairy-footed ones' or 'the soft-footed ones'. They had been a feature of Paraguayan society since the days of El Supremo. They did not threaten, but there was a strong implication that protesting would be futile. No point in insisting that my rights be respected. I did not have any rights in this place.

I was driven through the city, past the public buildings, past the Central Police Station, through the outskirts and along dusty, deserted roads. I had a moment's panic, I was in a foreign land, everyone had been friendly, but Paraguay was chronically unstable, and war was a distinct possibility. I imagined that I was about to left dead in a ditch. The back door on my side was not locked, and I could have rolled out and made off. Friendless, unarmed and in unfamiliar terrain, I would not have got far. I decided to wait things out. The car came to an intersection and turned right, and I realised we were driving back into the city. We stopped at the Military School, with its bullet-pocked walls painted over. Someone was sending me a message: they could drive me out into the countryside and disappear me any time they wanted to.

I was invited to sit on a chair in a corridor, one of the black suits sitting beside me. Time passed and coffee, black no sugar, was brought, along with some fresh French bread. Every morning since I had arrived, I had had black coffee, no sugar, and French bread. No one had asked what I wanted. This sudden arrest, the wait, the signal that I had been watched, the lack of any explanation, could only be some kind softening up process. If they intended to alarm me, they had succeeded.

The second officer reappeared. 'Follow me.' He opened a door for me and followed me in. There was a single chair in the middle of the room. 'Sit.' I sat and heard the officer sit on another chair, just to my right and out of sight behind me. A uniformed Arturo Bray was sitting behind a table. There were two other officers, one on each side of him.

One day in 1929, I was flying a Siskin fighter, descending through solid cloud, uncertain of my position, the altimeter winding down towards zero, hills hidden in the cloud. The cloud took on a greenish tinge. Would I break into clear air or just slam into the ground? I had that kind of feeling now.

To Bray's left sat Stroessner, in uniform, taking notes. On his right sat an officer in Air Force uniform with pilot's wings and the insignia of a major. It took me a split second to realise that it was San Martin. There had been no introductions. My tin trunks were lying opened and empty on the floor. My possessions, all of them, were laid out on several tables. My documents were on the centre table, in front of the three men. My possessions had been thoroughly inspected by customs the day my ship arrived. It seemed likely that a full list of them had been passed on to Bray. And enquiries made. And now my house had been searched and my possessions seized. I had no idea why I was here, other than I was suspected of something, and it seemed I would not be told. It was all very Kafkaesque.

We were conversing in Spanish, and I had to concentrate hard to understand the nuances and to ask for clarification when I heard an unfamiliar word. I answered Bray's question. 'I am a sailor.'

'This commission scroll states that you are an officer.'

'It was a short service-commission of five years. I had hoped to receive a permanent commission. Then the Depression started, and few permanent commissions were being granted. At the end of the five years, in early 1930, I was discharged.'

'What did you do during your five years in the RAF?'

'After passing through elementary and advanced training at Grantham —'

Bray interrupted, 'But you were already an experienced pilot?'

'The RAF have their own way of doing things. After graduating I was posted to Number 17 Fighter Squadron, flying Bristol Bulldogs at Upavon for a year. Then I spent a year at the Royal Aircraft and Experimental Establishment at Boscombe Down.'

'How many types did you fly there?'

Bray had my RAF logbook open in front of him and I was sure he could answer the question himself.

'About forty or forty-five, a mix of military and civilian types. I loved it. The RAF is the best flying club in the world, and they paid me to do what I love. After Boscombe, I was posted to the Meteorological Flight at Duxford.'

'Your flying was assessed as exceptional at each stage of your RAF career?'

'Yes. That was partly due to the flying I had done before joining the Royal Air Force.'

Bray picked up a buff-coloured folder about the size of a passport. He opened it to the front page. My photograph was pasted inside the cover and the facing page had a blue stripe diagonally across it. He looked up and said, 'This is your British Civil "B" licence, entitling you to fly for hire or reward, as a commercial pilot?'

'Yes.'

'Why did you need it?'

'I did some flying for a small airline when I was on leave. These are uncertain times, I thought that it might be useful sometime.'

'Your passport states that you are of British nationality.'

'That is misleading, most citizens of the British Empire hold passports that identify them as British. I am a New Zealander. My father's father immigrated from Scotland in the 1860s. My father was born in New Zealand and all my family identify strongly with the land and people of New Zealand. The Great War made many people think of themselves as Kiwis, not Brits.'

'Kiwis? Brits?'

'A kiwi is a small flightless bird that only exists in my homeland. It is a symbol that New Zealanders identify with. The other symbol is the silver fern that the All Blacks wear. And "Brit" is short for British. The bonds of empire were weakened during the war. When the Great War broke out in 1914, thousands of New Zealand men, and women, volunteered for the New Zealand Expeditionary Force that served as part of the British Empire's forces that fought in Palestine and France and Flanders. And before that, at Gallipoli in Turkey. Thousands died. Many blamed the British high command. We perceived them as bunglers who used our soldiers as cannon fodder. Especially the First Lord of the Admiralty, that incompetent bastard Winston Churchill. The Gallipoli Campaign was his idea. Many thousands of soldiers died there and then all the survivors were evacuated, and nothing had been achieved; they had all died for nothing. My countrymen had died for nothing.'

'All Blacks?'

'Our national rugby team.'

'Rugby?'

'A game played by two teams of fifteen men each. With an oval leather ball. It is our sport, almost a religion.'

'And your teams are made up of black men?'

'No, they are called All Blacks because they dress in black. Their black jerseys have a small silver fern embroidered on them.'

Bray sat in silence for a moment. The conversation had descended into farce, there was a lightening of the mood in the room. Bray said, 'You live in a country that has adopted a small flightless bird as a national symbol, your passport says you are British. Not only are you not British but you also hate the British, or at least their generals and government. Your national religion is a game played with a leather ball and your national team is called the All Blacks but they are no blacks in it? And another symbol is a fern that is not a plant; it is a small piece of embroidery?'

'Yes. There are some Māori in the All Blacks team, the indigenous people of my country, but they are not black, but dark brown.'

Bray was clearly torn between interrogating me and satisfying his curiosity. He rallied. 'How did you come to be in Paraguay? We know you arrived on the SS *Eden*, but why were you a seaman on that ship?'

'There was no work for me in New Zealand. I was at Port Chalmers, just up the road from my hometown, playing poker with some men, including the first mate of the ship I arrived aboard.' I told him the story of my pierhead jump. Bray appeared puzzled.

'A pierhead jump is when you sign on just before departure. *Eden* set off intending to pick up cargoes of opportunity. We only knew our next port of call. We sailed to Bluff, found a cargo for Port Taranaki, then one for Nouméa, in French New Caledonia, then Papeete on Tahiti in French Polynesia, and so on for months. Santiago, Callao, Punta Arenas, Montevideo, then Buenos Aires. We had been in Buenos Aires a week before I heard that we had a cargo to deliver to the Casado Company in Asunción.'

Bray said, 'Such a small ship for the long haul from Papeete to Santiago.'

'Yes. It required careful planning and conservation of coal.'

I described the planning and the voyage. Bray gestured to a large book, lying open on his table. 'We have the ship's logbook here and it confirms that you joined a few hours before the departure from Port Chalmers, and the ship's movements from there down to its arrival in the República del Paraguay. The ship was docked at Callao for three weeks. What did you do and where did you go?'

'I took a train to Lima and went sightseeing. Played poker. Won often enough to pay for a hotel room and three square meals a day. Sat in cafés and read. I read a lot. I watched the world go by. I enjoy watching the world go by.'

Bray said, 'We have noticed. You know that Bolivia claims that she owns the territory between the foothills of the Andes and the west bank of the Rio Paraguay? And that we know that the territory is ours and always has been. And that there have been skirmishes between Paraguayan and Bolivian troops?'

'Yes.'

'War seems likely. Peru and Bolivia share a border, and many Bolivians do business in Lima. Bolivia has an embassy there. Did you meet any Bolivians?'

Without hesitation I said, 'No.'

I had, but this was not the moment to say so. There had been some Bolivian businessmen, and a chap from the Bolivian Embassy who was vague about his duties. I had assumed that he dabbled in intelligence. 'I played poker with some Peruvian businessmen, at least they said that's what they were.'

'Did you talk about Paraguay?'

'No. I didn't know anything about your country, I barely knew where it was. No one talked about it.'

'What did you talk about?'

'Poker. The Depression. How long it would go on for, when would the world economy recover. The Peruvians talked a lot about their favourite whorehouses and bars. They could hold their drink. They invited me to join them on their tour of the brothels.'

'Did you join them?'

'No.'

'Don't you like women?'

'I like women.'

'Yes. You have been spending a lot of time with Sophia.'

Sophia, first name only. It was disconcerting that Bray was on first name terms with the one person in Paraguay who I was on intimate terms with. Bray was a skilled interrogator and doubled back, saying, 'You told Sophia that your father taught you to fly.'

'Yes. He did.'

'But there is no record of this in your papers.'

'I recorded it in a logbook that I left at home.'

'But the RAF would have needed to see it.'

'No, I thought it best to let the RAF teach me to fly from scratch. They would not have liked the idea that I might know something they don't. Sometimes it is best to feign ignorance.'

'You are not always honest. You did not tell Sophia about your career in the RAF.'

'No. New Zealanders have a tradition of being able to turn their hands to anything. This sometimes confuses outsiders. New Zealanders must be versatile; we are so far from anywhere that often if you can't do something yourself that something does not get done. I have found that sometimes people have trouble believing me when I describe what I have done with my life. I did not want Sophia to think that I was a conman.'

'Do you lie often?'

'No more than any sensible man. Never about important things.'

'What things are important to you?'

'Love, honour, professionalism.'

'Did you fight in the Great War?'

'No. I was sixteen when the armistice was signed. I was in the school's Cadet Corps, a paramilitary organisation to prepare boys for the Army.'

Bray held up a document. 'This is the order for your admission as a barrister of the Supreme Court of New Zealand?'

'Yes. I was a law clerk and a law student after I left school. After I qualified, I worked as a junior in the chambers of a distinguished Silk — a senior barrister holding the rank of King's Counsel. Most of our work was criminal law.'

'But you left the law? Why would you leave such a well-paid profession?'

'Juniors are not well paid, so I was not giving up anything material. I was, am, more interested in flying. Do you fly?'

Bray ignored the question and clearly thought I was being cheeky. I decided that being cheeky to Bray was not a good idea. He said, 'Bolivian Intelligence could have recruited you in Callao. An intelligent, well-educated man, a military officer, a man with nothing better to do.'

'But I did not know I was going to Paraguay.'

'The plan might have been for you to stay with the *Eden* until you could find a ship bound for Paraguay and sign onto it.'

'If I were a spy, I would not have brought my documentation to Paraguay. Without it I would have appeared to be what I actually am, a seaman on a tramp steamer. None of the crew knows much about my life before I joined the ship. They don't know that I was a lawyer and a pilot. Without the papers you have before you, it is unlikely that anyone would have taken me for anything other than a mariner.'

'We found a machine gun, a pistol, and a very sharp bayonet in your trunks. Are you planning to start a war?'

'No. There are rough men aboard every ship, and out at sea it is easy to get rid of someone you don't like. The bayonet and sharpening it was a message to my shipmates that I was a serious person. The pistol was a gift from my father. He wore it in the Great War. It was my sidearm when I was in the RAF.'

'And the BAR?'

'I won the Browning Automatic Rifle in a poker game.'

'You are a gambler?'

'Sometimes. Recreationally.'

I got the impression that in Bray's world any self-respecting man was well armed, and my possession of the weapons was of no real consequence. He changed tack. 'You were seen watching the flying at the airbase … for half a day?'

'Yes. I like aeroplanes, I did not attempt to hide that.'

'Perhaps you thought we would not notice. Your sketchbook includes pictures of the buildings.'

'Yes, and scores of other sketches, none of which have any military overtones.'

I had seen photographs spread out on a side table and guessed that Bray had had my film rolls developed and made prints from the negatives. He said, 'Your photographs include ones of the gunboats and the Naval and Military Arsenal. Why?'

'You know that I took photographs everywhere I went and none of them has any intelligence value.'

Bray thought for a moment and said, 'A knife with a fork and spoon is unremarkable. The knife alone marks an assassin. Perhaps your collection of unremarkable sketches and photographs are like the fork and spoon? And your photographs include the Central Police Station, the Army and Navy headquarters, and the Military School.'

I thought it best to say nothing. Bray continued, 'Your photographs of our two new gunboats are ones the Bolivians would like to see.'

It was time to reason. I imagined I was in a courtroom, trying to persuade a jury or a judge. I sensed that Bray was more judge than juror and was more likely to be persuaded by the kind of rational, logical argument I would use with a judge. 'Since arriving in Paraguay, I have not learned anything that I could not learn by reading newspapers and technical journals. Or at the picture show. Your gunboats and aircraft were shown in a newsreel I saw in Buenos Aires. The city guidebooks contain illustrations of all the major buildings in the capital. Every ministry of war monitors open-source material about their rivals, and no doubt Bolivia does.'

He said, 'You seem to know a lot about how intelligence is gathered?'

'RAF officers who travel in Europe are briefed to keep their eyes open and report. The officer who briefed me told me I what I have just told you.'

'But you have been accepted into Paraguayan society and might soon be able to learn and pass on information that is not in the public domain.' Bray changed tack again. 'What did you do between leaving Britain and signing on to your ship?'

'I travelled to China to join my family. My father is working on improvements to the streetcar network in the French Concession in Shanghai. I worked there as a draftsman for six months.'

'A draftsman?'

'Yes, I worked in my father's office in some of my school holidays and picked up the basics.'

'Anything else?'

'Then I accepted a contract to work for a warlord in North-Eastern China.'

'What did you do for him?'

'I supervised the assembly of new aircraft and test flew them. I found sites for airstrips and airfields and supervised their construction. I helped set up a small flying school. I advised the General on how to best use his small Air Force.'

'How long did you work for him?'

'Six months. It was supposed to be a year, but the General ran out of money.'

Bray paused, then went on, 'Nesterov has flown with you and gone over your pilot's logbooks. He says that your flying and airmanship are first class. Our consul in London has inspected the six-monthly Royal Air Force Officer Lists and you appear in them. Sophia tells me that you like Paraguay and the Paraguayans. The Director of the Geographic Institute tells us that you showed no unseemly interest in the details of recent explorations of the Chaco. Counsel Garza reports that he is satisfied that you are a lawyer.'

Garza must have been the lawyer I saw defending the murderer, who had chatted to me about lawyering at the General's dinner party. I felt a chill. I had been watched and assessed, possibly since I was noticed sightseeing in the city. Were the invitations calculated to provide opportunities to assess me? If so, for what? If they really thought I was a spy, I would have been thrown into a cell until they got around to shooting me. What was going on? I was relieved yet baffled. I guessed that the invitations had been genuine, and that idle gossip had come to the attention of someone important. I certainly hoped so.

Bray said, 'We would like to invite you to dinner at the mess and to stay the night. We will talk again in the morning.' He paused, then continued, 'Your country is an island surrounded by water and a long way from anywhere. Mine is a long way from anywhere and is an island surrounded by land.'

After dinner in the mess, a very relaxed and pleasant affair, I was given a comfortable room and a soldier was posted outside the door, 'in case I needed anything'. In the morning, Stroessner and Bray were gone, and I met with San Martin. We chatted while he drove us out to the airfield.

San Martin confirmed what I had guessed; it was almost certain that war with Bolivia would break out, possibly this year, if not soon after. The only issue was when and where, and how prepared Paraguay could be.

The white building at the airfield was for command and the Aviation School. San Martin showed me around. He drew my attention to the framed photographs decorating the walls and explained their meaning. Some were of the graduating classes of aviators, handsome young men in crisp white uniforms, with their diplomas in their hands. Others were formal photographs of French officers, complete with their medals and ribbons, from the Great War. Possibly some of them were from France's endless colonial wars. He told me a French mission had helped set up the Air Force and had persuaded Paraguay to buy French Potez and Wibault warplanes.

The problem was that there were very few Paraguayans qualified as pilots or observers. The first class had graduated in 1928, the second in

1930, and another was about to. There were so few pilots that it had been decided that no aircraft should fly with two pilots aboard, the loss of two in one accident could not be risked. The other problem was that none of the aviators had more than a few years' experience. They would have to improve their airmanship and learn to fight at the same time.

Air Service Command believed I could help, and I was offered a job as a civilian consultant. The offer included a house with a maid to clean and cook, food, and a modest salary. When I had proved my worth, I would be given the use of a car. In return, I was to be a jack of all trades. I would do anything that would free up Paraguayan aviators for training or combat.

I accepted and signed a one-year contract with the República del Paraguay and became an employee of the Arma Aérea Paraguaya, also known as the Aviación en Campaña.

> *Connor Travis drew wages and discharged.*
> – Ship's Articles. SS *Eden*. 29 January 1932

* *

I moved into a small house on a quiet street, the maid proved quiet and competent, and there, compared with a bunk in the fo'c'sle of SS *Eden*, I lived a life of luxury.

There would be some flying, of an unspecified nature. My tasks included developing an order of battle for the Bolivian Air Force, translating foreign aviation manuals into Spanish, and reading and analysing any publication that might provide information relevant to an air war in the Chaco. My mother, the romance novelist, had no technical Spanish to teach me, so I would have to teach myself. I found that French terms were used alongside Spanish ones in day-to-day flying, and I had photographs of several of the types of aircraft mounted on large sheets of cardboard, one for Spanish and one for French. Discussions with the technicians and aircrews revealed most of the necessary words, and multilingual dictionaries the remainder. Soon the sheets were full of exotic technical worlds, with arrows to the appropriate component(s). I worked on a concise multilanguage aviation dictionary to be used in the Aviation School for pilots, observers, and maintenance personnel.

There was a large stack of crates of books, journals, and pamphlets in the corner of one of the hangars, but no one had had the time to organise them. A librarian spent two afternoons a week at headquarters, and I helped her catalogue the materials. Except for the celestial navigation I had done on *Eden*, the past six months had provided no intellectual stimulation to speak of, and I awoke each morning eager to go to work and learn new things. My new colleagues were men of action and more than a little amused that I could enjoy being a librarian.

Each day was a little different from the last, and I enjoyed the variety. I went through stacks of newspapers and technical journals, anything that might have information about Bolivian aviation. I compiled a book of clippings and in a few weeks was able to start writing an appreciation of Bolivian air power, including aircraft in service and on order, and civil types of transport aeroplanes that would probably be impressed into service if war came.

The main combat types in the Bolivian inventory are six Vickers Type 143 single-seat fighters and six Vickers Vespa two-seat reconnaissance bombers. The armament of the Type 143 is identical to that of our Wibault 73 and the published figures suggest that the performance of each type is identical. The Vespa has an armament and performance identical to our Potez 25 ... It is understood that Bolivia has ordered up-to-date combat aeroplanes from the United States. These include Curtiss Falcon and Curtiss-Wright CW-17 Osprey two-seaters and Curtiss Hawk II single-seat fighters. The Hawk II has a performance superior to all aircraft currently in service in Paraguay and to the Fiat CR20bis fighters we have on order ... In the event of war, the usefulness of each type will be the product the training, skill and determination of the pilots and observers.

— Extract from: *Order of Battle of the Bolivian Air Service*
C. Travis. 20 February 1932

Negotiations for the sale of the steamer SS Eden *have failed, and it sailed yesterday in ballast for Montevideo.*

— *El Liberal*, Asunción. 25 February 1932

When *Eden* sailed it severed my last link with home and I was probably the only New Zealander within a thousand kilometres.

Chapter Seven
A Missing Plane. 24 February 1932

Poor Paraguay, so far from God, so close to Bolivia.
— Lieutenant-Colonel José Félix Estigarribia

I was in one of the workshops just before work started when San Martin arrived and knocked on the open door. I looked up and he said, 'There is something I would like you to look at. In the photo section. Do you have a moment?'

'Yes.'

One of the technicians, a very competent man called Ángel Garcia, was leading a group building a two-seat glider and intended that he and his comrades would learn to fly on it. This was strictly non-official, but they were permitted to use the workshops. I volunteered to help finish the glider, test fly it, and start teaching the men to fly. I was fitting a rib to the main spar of the port wing when San Martin arrived.

The photo section was only a few yards away and soon we were both sitting on stools at a bench with trays of photographs and rows of folders on a shelf above. On the bench in front of San Martin was a small frame with eyepieces at the top, and on the bench below were two apparently identical aerial photographs. He adjusted a small knob on the right-hand side of the device and said, 'Here, have a look.'

We swapped stools. I looked into the eyepieces. The photographs were slightly blurred. I turned the knob until there was a single crisp image. What I was looking at was a pair of aerial photographs taken half a second apart. When viewed through the stereoscopic viewer, there was a single three-dimensional image, which made it much easier to interpret than a single photograph. All I saw was a thorn forest, a few small creeks.

'What am I looking for?'

'Look in the top right of the image.'

I saw some straight lines and some surfaces that reflected light. San Martin said, 'What do you think?'

I thought and looked again. I suddenly realised I was looking at the tail of an aeroplane. Slightly to the right and a little forward of the tail was a wingtip. He handed me a loupe. I lifted one of the photos out of the frame, tilted the equipoise lamp so it was close, and studied the photo. I could not make out any more detail but there was no doubt in my mind what I was looking at.

'There is an aeroplane, mostly hidden by vegetation.'

'Yes, let us talk in your office.'

San Martin closed my office door behind us and sat facing me across my desk. I asked him, 'Where was the photograph taken?'

'About seventy-five kilometres north-west of Puerto Casado. A Potez was returning from Bahia Negra to Concepción and decided to fly a dogleg into the Chaco just in case the Bolivians have penetrated further east than we know about. The observer saw a reflection, a glint, where there should not be anything man-made.'

'Is it one of ours?'

'No. And we don't know whose it is. Or what type it is, or how it got there. No one has reported a missing plane. In the normal course of events that would be news. A report would show up in the newspapers. The local newspapers reprint anything interesting from foreign papers. Nothing.'

There was a pause. I said, 'Someone better go and have a look at it.'

'Yes, you. At least you if you don't have anything important on?'

'I don't. But how do I find it? There are no roads, and my understanding is that the terrain is mostly featureless?'

'It is. Except that it was an unusually clear day. The pilot could see the Rio Paraguay and two distinctive bends in the river. He noted the compass bearings to those two points. If you plot the reciprocals on a map, you have the location.'

'But perfect visibility is uncommon?'

'Yes. But there was plenty of film in the cameras. The observer took dozens of oblique photos as they flew due south to a certain stream, which is full of water at this time of year and has a distinctive course, then due east to the river. I think the aeroplane is on one of the ranches. If it is, the manager will be able to guide a ground party to the site. Or a guide could be found at Puerto Casado. And the vertical camera took a series of overlapping photographs. When they are developed, we will have a photomosaic made up. A map. That won't make finding the aircraft easy, but it will make it possible. I want you to fly to Casado, we will provide a pilot, and then go overland to the aircraft, inspect it and report.'

Strolling around the Chaco had not been part of the job offered to me, but I felt obliged to accept his proposal, which I did.

'You will need clothing suitable for an extended journey overland to the crash site. I want you to do the planning. Make a list of any equipment you think you need. Note any ideas you may have about how to do this.'

I had an idea. 'I need to examine all the photographs you have. Can the photographic section do a rush job?' I told him why, and then said, 'I need the mosaic, as big as possible, and large prints of all the obliques. Can they be ready when work starts tomorrow morning? And every map you have of the area.'

'Yes, but you may be disappointed. The maps are rudimentary, and as you say, the terrain is largely featureless.'

San Martin was as good as his word and first thing in the morning I was at my desk studying the photographs. I was sure I knew what type of craft it was. I remembered an American NACA memorandum about the type and fetched it from the library.

ALL-METAL JUNKERS AIRPLANE, TYPE F 13

The Junkers all-metal airplane F 13 has a large, elegantly furnished cabin, with accommodations for four passengers and room for another passenger or assistant beside the pilot. The passenger cabin contains four comfortable padded chairs, of which the two front ones can be removed to make room for bulky baggage. Three windows, on two sides of the cabin, can be partially opened and afford a lateral and downward view … The characteristics and performance are as follows … Useful load 700 kg. Speed 170 kilometres per hour … Some of the Junkers all-metal airplanes have been exposed for months to snow and rain without detriment … The particular utility of the type F 13 for tropical countries has been demonstrated by various expeditions and by the daily air traffic in South America. The termites, which are so destructive to wooden airplanes in tropical countries, cannot hurt metal airplanes. In short, the life of a metal aeroplane is practically unlimited …

– National Advisory Committee for Aeronautics. *Aircraft Circular No. 6: All-Metal Junkers Airplane, Type F 13*. Washington. May 1926

The memorandum described the aeroplane I had identified in the photographs. There were diagrams, dimensions and weights, and some performance figures. I studied the memorandum and made notes. I also studied all the available maps of the area and prepared a sketch map, developed a plan, wrote a summary of it, and compiled a list of what preparation needed to be done. I included a list of equipment I would need.

I took the materials to San Martin and said, 'The aeroplane is almost certainly a Junkers F 13, a single-engine, all-metal transport. Unofficially, it can carry anything that can be squeezed inside the cabin. The type is operated by several airlines in South America and some air forces.'

'Including Bolivia's?'

'A Bolivian airline operates some and they would probably be requisitioned in the event of war.'

'How does it handle?'

'Pilots compare it to a brewer's dray, sluggish, but at least as useful. There is no sign of fire, and it appears to be intact. Paraguay needs every aeroplane it can acquire, and I guess that the country has little spare cash?'

'Yes. If it is repairable, we want to salvage it.'

'Repairing and salvaging it would be complex and time-consuming and need a lot of resources. And it would help if Garcia could come.' I explained why I needed him.

'And it is essential to have him?'

'Yes.'

'Okay. We can spare him for a while. I will make sure there will be no shortage of labour, horses, mules, oxen and carts. We must move quickly. The Bolivians are active and may be operating aircraft in the area. If we can find the F 13, so can they. There is no open area suitable for landing near the crash site. I will fly you and Garcia to Casado. Find the means to travel overland to it. We will set up a schedule and I will monitor your progress by overflying your location.'

We discussed navigation issues, preparation for the flight north, and the division of labour. I said, 'I need to know the deviation between compass north and magnetic north and the variation between magnetic north and true north.'

It turned out that the variation was marked on a map, and that the aeroplane's compass had been swung recently, so I read the deviation off a card in the cockpit. I added these details to my sketch map of the area. With this information and the compass headings from the crew, I could plot reciprocal headings. Where they crossed was where the mysterious Junkers awaited me. I was confident that with the map and the aerial photographs, I would find it.

* *

I arrived at the airbase well before sunrise the day after my discussion with San Martin to find the lights on in two of the hangars. In one of them sat the Potez 25 that San Martin and I would use. San Martin was the pilot. I would occupy the observer's cockpit behind the pilot. The equipment I had asked for was laid out on canvas sheets beside the aeroplane. I checked the items against my list and helped the men load them into two containers, each about the size of a 115-kilogram bomb. When the containers were full, they were placed on trolleys, jacked up and attached to the bomb racks, one beneath each lower wing.

The Potez was pushed out of the hangar and the wheels chocked while we dressed in flying gear, including parachutes. We climbed aboard. Garcia occupied a very cramped space behind the observer's cockpit. He loved flying and the discomfort worried him not at all. Mechanics stood on the wing root of the lower wing, one on each side, and cranked the engine into life. The night was clear and there was a half-moon. Two lines of kerosene lamps had already been laid out, and two red lamps marked the far end of the strip we would use for take-off. We took off and climbed, turning onto a heading that would take us north along the Rio Paraguay to Puerto Casado. The first soft light of the new day was showing in the east, the air was warm and smooth.

I was wearing thick whipcord trousers and an equally thick shirt, sturdy ankle boots, overalls, a light leather jacket, and a leather flying helmet plus googles. The heat and humidity on the ground had been oppressive, but at 1,000 metres, with a slipstream of 195 kilometres an hour, it was pleasantly warm, and I settled in the cockpit with my maps and notebook. It would take us about an hour and a half to Puerto Casado. We would not have to refuel at Conceptión, saving time and eliminating many sets of prying eyes.

This was my first flight in a Potez, and I looked around the cockpit. I was sitting within a scarf ring, a mounting for the two Madsen machine guns. The ring and the machine guns could be rotated through 360 degrees and a frame on top of the ring allowed the machine guns to be elevated and depressed through about 90 degrees. All of this had to be done by the observer, without any mechanical assistance. The contortions necessary were a challenge at cruising speed and very difficult at high speed. Below me and to the rear was a mounting for a third machine gun and a panel that could be slid back so this gun could be fired to cover the underside of the aeroplane. I doubted that a gunner could be agile enough to swap between the gun mounts quickly enough to make this arrangement workable. A good observer would need to be as skilled at his job as the pilot needed to be to fly. There was a spare stick in a fabric pocket on the right side of the cockpit. This could be inserted into a socket on the floor so the observer could fly the craft if the pilot were killed or wounded. This was peacetime and we needed all the room we could make, so the machine guns had been removed.

This was my first cross-country flight in Paraguay, and I used it to widen my knowledge of the country, making notes and sketching any feature that might help me to navigate in poor visibility. I marked the time at each of the hundred-kilometre marks on the map. At each checkpoint, I did a mental calculation and confirmed that our groundspeed was as high or higher than the estimated one.

The sluggish river ran north and south, with its numerous channels. An occasional paddle steamer was visible, trailing pale grey smoke as cordwood was consumed in its furnaces.

Large sections of the west bank of the Paraguay were underwater, with copses of tall trees standing on a multitude of small islands dotted amongst the inundations. From time to time, we flew over what appeared to be large meadows of lush grass, but occasional glints showed that they too were flooded.

My thoughts drifted to Sophia. Our relationship had intensified, and my musings always had an erotic edge. A couple of days after my brush with Bray, I had asked her about her relationship with him and his ilk. She assured me that if she thought I was in danger, she would have warned me. And that I was a foreigner, albeit a nice one, and her first duty was to Paraguay. This did not erase the memory of her assessment being quoted to me during an interrogation, but eros had me firmly in its grip. Soon after the General's party, Sophia had defined the limits of our relationship. She had no interest in settling down with one man. If I wanted to see her, I should ring first. If I called in and saw a small medallion on a chain around the doorknob, she was entertaining, and I must not disturb her. I tried and failed to feel jealous. She was so open and honest and generous when we were together.

Now and again, I checked on Garcia, who smiled and gave me a thumbs up. He wanted to be a pilot, had taught himself navigation, and kept a record of every flight in a pilot's logbook I had given him. This record would help him satisfy the authorities when he applied for flight training.

Concepción appeared to the east and twenty minutes later we overflew Puerto Pinasco, the scene of the massacre in 1927, with its factory and its narrow-gauge railway, running west into the haze over the Chaco.

My acquaintances had warned me against ever going into the Chaco. To them it was a place to be avoided, a place of heat and no water and an oversupply of life forms that would do their best to kill the traveller, or at least make him miserable and want to be somewhere else, anywhere else. Some of them had travelled there, most had not. I had discarded as highly unlikely some of the stories they related, but the believable ones made me think about survival. I received some practical advice, such as the kind of clothing to wear. Namely, garments that resisted the thorns and mosquitos. Another said that I should always carry a firearm and suggested that I load my Webley pistol with dum-dum ammunition. I acted on that advice, and the pistol was in its holster at my waist. Each bullet had its tip filed flat and four grooves down it. These modifications meant the bullet would break up and expand on impact, a very desirable situation if a puma or ocelot broke cover and showed an interest in converting me into a snack.

After an hour and fifty minutes, I sighted the factory at Puerto Casado, with its six distinctive thin chimneys. At the water's edge, a paddle steamer was unloading at a dilapidated wharf and two, perhaps three, small steam locomotives were working on the web of railway tracks around the factory. A locomotive and a line of boxcars and flatcars were on the mainline. I saw a neat village of small houses and a large church and a single street of bigger, two-storey, rather grand dwellings with red-tiled roofs. Beyond the village was an encampment with rows of tents, half a dozen large low buildings, and a parade ground with the national flag flying on a tall flagpole. Just to the north of the tents was a level area of sun-baked dirt and grass. Only the windsock identified it as the airfield. We flew overhead, checked the wind direction and San Martin landed towards the river.

We taxied in the direction of some low buildings. As soon as the propeller flicked to a stop, I was assailed by a wet heat that made me gasp. By the time I had climbed out and taken off my parachute, overalls, jacket, and helmet, I was sweating, and perspiration was running down my back and staining my shirt.

We walked to the buildings, sometimes on crunchy yellow grass, passing occasional clumps of brightly coloured flowers.

A soldier in grey-green cotton fatigues and a bush hat walked over to us, saluted San Martin and said, 'Please follow me.'

Garcia went in search of fuel drums and a pump, while I followed the soldier and San Martin into a large administration building, built of roughly cut timber and adobe, with a steeply pitched thatched roof. Two clerks were typing, and officers came and went. Our guide knocked on an office door. 'Enter.'

We went inside. A man in the uniform of a Lieutenant-Colonel stood up and came around his desk, smiled and nodded at San Martin, who saluted. The Colonel was José Estigarribia, who held out his hand to me. We shook.

After meeting him at the General's party, we had met for a drink several times and once he had invited me for dinner at his home. This was modest but freshly painted and clean and tidy, in the style adopted by Paraguayans of humble origins who hoped to rise in society by merit and hard work. He had asked many intelligent questions about military aviation.

Estigarribia said, 'Good to see you again. I hear you have been making yourself useful.'

'I hope so.'

I must have looked surprised because he said, 'Paraguay is a village. You are a foreigner, a New Zealander no less, and you have been given a responsible job. And I have received a telegram asking me to help you with anything you might need for your mission.'

I said, 'Do you know anything about the Junkers?'

He shrugged his shoulders. 'No. The telegram was the first I have heard of any mysterious aircraft.'

San Martin explained the situation and what we wanted to do. Estigarribia had struck me as someone who would not tolerate long-windedness and San Martin was happy to be concise and to the point. He sketched out the situation.

Estigarribia said, 'There is a guide. I will send him a message and let you know when he arrives. It is best if you all travel as civilians, that way, if you come across Bolivian soldiers, you are just a hunting party going about your lawful occasions. Have a look around the base. My aide will show you to the officers' mess. Both of you are invited to dinner, at seven this evening.' He meant 7 pm, sharp.

San Martin saluted, I thanked the Colonel, and we went in search of breakfast.

* *

The officers' mess turned out to be a space with tables and chairs, a thatched roof, and no walls. I breakfasted on coarse but tasty bread, cheese, and some fruit I could not identify but took an immediate liking to, and strong, bitter coffee. We were in sight of the Casado Railway and a road. Two steam traction engines passed, each towing two trailers, the trailers stacked high with logs. A small locomotive was shunting rolling stock.

A fair-haired young man dressed in civilian clothes was having breakfast. We invited him to join us and asked him what brought him to this place. We were curious because he was the first man we had seen who was not in the Army or working for the Casado Company. His name was David Atten and he explained that after completing a degree in zoology at Trinity College, Oxford, he had trouble finding work. His response was to create a job for himself. He had decided that there was a market for nature films and photographs of exotic animals from little-known countries. He had spent time in the Andes, four months in Argentina and Uruguay, and had then moved on to Paraguay. Travellers' tales were full of accounts of the unusual diversity of wildlife in the Chaco, hence his presence in Puerto Casado. He turned out to have a fine, dry wit and was a delightful companion. David suggested we travel together. He seemed sensible and perhaps zoology was a useful body of knowledge to have where we were going. We agreed to his proposal.

A Corporal walked up to us, followed by a roughly dressed individual. The Corporal saluted San Martin and asked if we were the men in need of advice about the Chaco. San Martin answered in the affirmative. The Corporal introduced the man as a guide and left. Our guide was almost two metres tall but, exaggerating only slightly, appeared to be a metre wide. His vast belly protruded over the waistline of what appeared to be a baggy, dirty pair of pink-striped pyjama bottoms. His top half was covered by a large and dirty white dress shirt. The ensemble was topped off by a straw hat, the brim of which looked like a large rat had nibbled it. His grey hair sprouted from various holes in the crown of the hat.

We got out the photos, the photomosaic, and my sketch map. The guide spoke only Guarani, so San Martin had to translate. The guide had no trouble recognising the area covered and said he had passed through it several times while hunting and guiding General Belaieff.

I asked him how difficult it would be to get to the crash site, and how long it would take.

He shrugged. 'Depends on how you travel. I suggest we go by rail and horse. The rail part is west along the mainline to Kilometre 85, then north by way of the spur line to Hacienda Shaw, an estate owned by the Casado Company. We can do that in less than half a day. We can hire horses and men there and go overland.'

'How long will it take to get from the hacienda to the crash site?'

He shrugged. 'One or two days.'

He glanced at my boots. 'And you need leather leggings. Lots of thorn bushes and snakes and bugs where you are going.'

David looked at me. 'I have a spare pair you can have,' he said.

The details were quickly decided, and we went to hang our hammocks and get some rest.

It was still dark when we awoke. After a breakfast of bread, cheese, and coffee, Garcia joined us, dressed in civilian clothes. We packed some food, picked up our packs and went in search of the guide. We found him deep asleep and snoring loudly in a hammock on the porch of a derelict cottage, not far from the factory. Nothing we could say or do would wake him up. Though it did wake up his friend, barefooted, but wearing ragged trousers and shirt and, despite the hour, a large straw hat with the crown missing. He said, 'Yesterday was payday; he spent it on cana and a girl. He will not wake up any time soon.'

This presented a serious problem. I discussed it with Garcia and David. Eventually, we decided that given our doubts about the guide's usefulness, we would leave without him and hope we could find a guide at the railhead at the hacienda.

We arrived at the railway about an hour before dawn. David's baggage comprised an array of equipment, including two or three still cameras, several spare lenses, and a Bell and Howell handheld movie camera. We were discussing the technical side of his expedition when a machine appeared around a bend in the railway track and came to a halt beside us.

This was the autovia, a medium-sized Ford truck and trailer with their wheels and tyres replaced by iron wheels of the type used by the locomotives and rolling stock. The Army had delivered our gear to the railway, and it was securely tied to the tops of the truck and trailer. The back of the truck and the trailer had hard bench seats and roofs, but no glass in the windows. Garcia, David and I sat in the back of the truck.

Three soldiers and their equipment rode in the trailer. Telegraph and telephone lines were strung on roughly cut posts along the right of way. We discovered that the soldiers were travelling to the junction of the mainline and a southern spur to do some maintenance on the lines. The men were a Corporal and two Privates. All three were conscripts from Bahia Negra, a small settlement in the extreme north of Paraguay. They were really civilians in uniform, not career soldiers, and were getting through their obligatory service, counting the days until they could return to their families and friends.

We started out through the river mist, leaving the settlement of Puerto Casado behind. About thirty-five kilometres an hour was the best the autovia could manage, and the truck and trailer swayed gently on the uneven roadbed below the rails and sleepers. We were soon passing through a forest full of unfamiliar plant and animal life. David became animated, pointing out the most exotic species and maintaining a running commentary. The flora was of every conceivable type and stood at all angles.

David said, 'Those trees, the ones that lean in all directions, with the swollen trunks, the locals call them *palo borracho*, the stick that is drunk. This is the drunken forest.'

The driver decided to stop and check something under the bonnet. Within seconds I felt a jab into my thigh and looked down to see a large mosquito, intent on feeding off me. Before I could react, there was a cloud of mosquitoes covering each one of us. We urged the driver to hurry up but, obviously used to the insect life, he took his time. Finally, the autovia started to move, although it seemed a long time before we had left the last of the mosquitoes behind. The line was mostly through forested terrain but occasionally we would emerge in grassy openings. The naturalist said, 'I know it looks like a well-tended lawn but most of it is waist-high and full of unpleasant surprises.'

He started to list creatures that slithered, crawled or ran and that were better avoided. He pointed at tall, thick trees that grew in profusion on islands that rose a few metres above the average ground level.

'Quebracho trees. The name is an adaptation of the Guarani words for "axe breaker". One of the hardest woods there is. Around 1860, someone discovered that the trees are a rich source of tannin, used in tanning leather. The trees are logged and transported by the railway to the factories where they are macerated and soaked in water which produces a tannin-rich fluid. It is one of Paraguay's most important exports. Some of the timber is cut into railway sleepers, mostly for export. A house built of the wood will last a very long time.'

I realised that our acquaintance might have some survival tips and I had him explain how certain trees and plants could be persuaded to provide water in areas where there was no groundwater, or where water contained so many minerals that it was undrinkable by man or beast.

A little less than an hour and a half after setting off, we reached Kilometre 45, the junction of the mainline and the southern spur. The soldiers disembarked and were setting up camp when we got going again. A few kilometres along the line, we switched into a siding, alongside a clearing in the forest. Scores of quebracho logs were stacked close beside it. Soon we were treated to the sight of a skilled man and trained beasts working together as one. A team of eight oxen appeared from the forest, dragging a jinker, a pair of massive wooden spoked wheels, shod with iron and connected by a thick wooden axle. Chained to the axle was one end of the trunk of a tree, about three metres in diameter and fifteen metres or so long. A man walked alongside, constantly cracking a whip and talking to the oxen. While we watched, the log was dragged into place and dropped parallel to a flatcar, which already had a few logs loaded on it. The ox team and the driver walked around to the other side of the flatcar, and chains were attached to each end of the log. The chains were then dragged over the car and attached to the traces. As the oxen walked away, they dragged the log up a ramp onto the car.

A train arrived from the west, steamed past, stopping east of the siding. One of the loggers operated the switch and the train backed into the siding. We set off on the main track, continuing our journey.

The heat of the day had arrived, conversation tailed off and I tried to nap. I was thinking about how much I hated horses and that I would have no choice but to ride from the hacienda to the crash site, when I slipped off to sleep. I awoke to find the autovia travelling due north. I had slept through the switch to the northern spur. I was annoyed because I had been keeping notes and marking up my map and had missed about ten kilometres of observations. I felt a little better when Garcia told me that it was no different from the parts I had been awake for. Soon we were approaching the railhead, which consisted of a siding lined with cattle pens and a rough wooden platform with no roof.

* *

The manager was waiting. He smiled, held out his hand, and said, 'Gidday cobber, small world, isn't it?'

It was Sandy Murray, my friend from the Café Eiffel. 'It is. I knew you managed an estancia, but not that it was this one.'

He helped us load our gear on the back of his Ford Model T pickup. David drew the short straw and rode in back while Sandy, Garcia and I jammed ourselves into the cab for the short drive to the estate house, which was home and headquarters of the estancia, a cattle ranch the size of southern Wales.

Sandy poured us many large glasses of iced lemonade and recommended we sling hammocks and meet with him after the heat of the day had passed. Our quarters consisted of a building with no walls, a thatched roof, and posts to sling hammocks. At about eight, we went over to the main house and sat around a large table on the veranda in comfortable wicker armchairs, enjoying the comparative cool of the evening, with few insects to bother us. I spread the photomosaic, sketch map and notebook on the dinner table and explained the situation to Sandy. Finally, I said, 'Do you recognise the site?'

'Yes, I do. It is about twenty-five kilometres north-east of here.'

'That close?'

'Yep.'

He brought out a large sketch map of the estancia, and I could see that it overlapped with the mosaic. I marked my map with details that were on Sandy's map but not on mine.

'It looks like it is on your property. Is it accessible?'

He smiled. 'It is on the property, and all places are accessible. Do you mean can it be reached easily?'

'Yes.'

'You could ride there in half a day, without too much trouble, if you do not lose your way. You would have to walk the last five hundred metres or so and cut through the thorn forest.'

'Can you provide a guide?'

'I can do better than that, I will take you. I have not inspected that part of the ranch for a while. I can kill two birds with one stone.'

I had been told to mark out landing grounds wherever possible and asked Sandy if he would mind if I did this near the house. He consented and we paced out a strip 700 metres by 15 metres and marked the corners with cairns of stones. Sandy promised to splash them with whitewash when he had a spare moment. He would also improvise a windsock. As we walked back to the house, Sandy said, 'The sun is over the yardarm; let's have a beer, or two.'

The beer was surprisingly cool, given that the hacienda had no fridge or icemaker. I asked, 'How do you keep the beer cool?'

'We hang sacks of bottles and keep the sacking wet. The water evaporates and that cools the beer.'

The conversation turned to the natural history of the Chaco, and Sandy regaled us with tales of the predators we must avoid on the morrow. We listened with rapt, and somewhat nervous, attention. Except for David. He showed more interest than alarm.

Sandy said, 'It is unlikely that we will come across a jaguar. If we do, it is unlikely to attack four men on horseback.'

I asked a question. 'What about when we are on foot?'

'If we keep alert and don't surprise any snakes, we should be all right. Do you have a firearm?'

'Yes. A .455-calibre Webley pistol. Six shot. I have filed the bullets into dum-dums.'

'Okay. I have two Mauser 1898 pattern rifles.' He looked at David and Garcia, 'Do you know how to use them?'

They both nodded. I asked Sandy, 'What do you carry?'

He went inside, and came back with a large leather holster, and drew a massive pistol from it. 'This is a .577-calibre, four-barrelled Lancaster howdah pistol, the kind hunters in India carry when shooting from an elephant, as a final defence against an angry tiger.'

We were impressed but not reassured. I mentioned that Garcia aspired to be a pilot. Sandy said, 'I need an aeroplane to get around, quicker and safer.'

I said, 'If you decide to buy one, look me up and I will advise you and help you to find one. I might find the time to teach you to fly it.'

The discussion turned to transport. I said that I was no horseman and told him a story to illustrate my point. 'I did a six-month stint in the RAF on the North-West Frontier of India and in Afghanistan. One day I was assigned as RAF liaison officer to accompany an Army column through territory occupied by hostile tribes. I was given a slow old horse and had no trouble for the first few days. The odd shot was fired at us, and we lost several mules, but no men. One day the Colonel ordered me to link up with another part of the column and insisted I ride his horse, black of coat and red of eye. I had just mounted when an aeroplane flew low overhead to drop a message bag. The horse took off. I lost a stirrup and the horse galloped three times around a circle of about a quarter of a mile. It was all I could do to hang on. The soldiers cheered and laughed themselves silly. When the Colonel stopped laughing, he told me he would shout me a drink in the mess tent that night, and I could have my old horse.'

After Sandy stopped laughing, he said that he had a placid old nag for me to ride and that riding was infinitely preferable to being on foot. He explained that although he knew this area well, even he had to be careful about navigation. 'Two friends of mine were exploring an unfamiliar part of the Chaco. The terrain and vegetation all looked the same to them. They lost their way and died of thirst.'

There was a pause. There is nothing like the prospect of dying of thirst to concentrate the mind. We discussed the issue and agreed that we would rely on the maps and mosaic with their few distinct features and our compasses, and estimate the distance covered. We compared our prismatic compasses. I took mine and my sketch map away from any ferrous metal and checked its deviation. I did the same with Sandy's. They matched within five degrees, and we worked out a compass bearing from the hacienda to the wreck site and from each distinctive feature to the next.

Sandy said, 'We also need a way to measure how far we have travelled, when on foot. This is how I do it.'

He brought out a thirty-centimetre length of rope, knotted at each end and in the middle. There were nine black beads threaded on one section and five red beads on the other. 'I count steps. I start with all red beads at the back knot and all black beads at the centre knot. I cover exactly a hundred metres in sixty-four steps. Every hundred metres I slide a black bead to the front knot. When all nine black beads are there, I count another sixty-four steps. I have walked another hundred metres, a total of a thousand metres. Then I slide one of the red beads to the middle knot. Then I push all the black beads back to the middle and start counting again.'

He showed me an example. Two red beads and four black beads meant he had walked 2,400 metres.

'At night or in poor visibility,' he continued, 'it is best to stop until you can see the way. If you must walk on you can tell the red beads from the black by touch. The black beads are spherical. I have filed the red beads into cubes. Each of you should carefully calculate how many steps you take to cover a hundred metres.'

He pointed to a straight section of the track leading from a corner of the stockyards to the veranda. 'The distance is exactly three hundred and fifty metres. Start on your right foot and count when your left foot touches the ground. Divide the total paces by three and a half and you have the number of paces you take to cover a hundred metres.'

We each took our turn. My count was identical to Sandy's: sixty-four paces to cover a hundred metres.

Sandy supplied the rations and the water bags. We set off well before dawn. Four men on horses and two pack horses. Each of us carried a freshly sharpened machete and a whetstone to resharpen it. Between us, we had my pistol, the two rifles, and Sandy's pistol. Sandy smiled when he caught me looking at his pistol and guessed that I might be wondering if my Webley was adequate.

He said, 'Don't worry, I have never come across an animal I could not hit and kill with this.' He eased the pistol halfway out of its holster and slid it back. David and Garcia had rifles slung across their backs and bandoliers of ammunition criss-crossed their chests, looking for all the world like Mexican bandits as portrayed in a B-movie.

The journey turned out to be easier and quicker than I had thought it would be. For the first few hours, a full moon bathed the landscape with monochromatic light. By the time it was replaced by a hot sun, we had covered about ten kilometres. Those ten kilometres and the next ten or so, were across meadows with stirrup-high grass, and through clumps of widely spaced trees, and across occasional creeks, none of them wide or deep. At one point we came to a clearing carpeted with blue flowers, which turned out to be floating in a small creek. I kept track of our progress on my sketch map. At each clump of trees, I chopped an arrowhead shape pointing back the way we had come. From time to time we stopped, and I conferred with Sandy. He recognised the terrain, but I wanted to be able to get there and back without a guide. Just in case. For the last few kilometres, the going was close, but we were only five hundred metres from the Junkers when we had to dismount. David volunteered to stay with the horses.

There was a single tree, as shown on the aerial photos, and by keeping it slightly to our left we could head straight for the wreck. My experiences in the bush of Southland had taught me how easy it was to get lost, sometimes in a short distance, and especially when the sun was obscured by clouds and there were no landmarks. I started a new sketch map and marked in the compass bearing to the tree and the estimated one to the aeroplane.

We set out, chopping our way through the thorns with our heavy and very sharp machetes. I checked my compass every few steps and Sandy kept track of the distance with his pace count and beads. With no shade and a high sun, my clothes were soon soddened with sweat. Every hundred metres we relieved the man on point. Sometimes, we paused and resharpened the machetes. I was leading when I suddenly saw the aeroplane, only a few metres away.

As I had suspected, it was a Junkers F 13, painted overall in dark grey with a matt non-reflective finish. The skin resembled corrugated iron but was made of a light alloy called Duralumin. It was an early model, with the leading edge of the fin and rudder swept back, and the trailing edge of the rudder a graceful curve. It was at least ten years old and likely to have seen hard service and flown many hours. The glint our pilot had seen must have been the plexiglass windscreen or cabin windows. It was resting in a gulley, and I could see that it had clipped the top of the forest for a hundred metres or so, before coming to rest in a steep nose-down attitude. It had settled in just the right place. The passage along the treetops had slowed it down and the descent through the foliage into the gulley had taken most of the remaining speed off. It must have arrived at the bottom of the gulley slowly, as it appeared to be in one piece, with no serious damage visible. We set to work with our machetes, clearing the vegetation so I could assess its condition. After two or three hours of hot and sweaty work, we took a break. We retraced our steps through what was now a clearly marked path.

We told David what we had found and put the billy on. I prepared a large tin mug of hot, strong Earl Grey tea with condensed milk and lots of sugar, while the others made yerba-maté, and we sat around enjoying the break in silence. The hot drinks had the curious effect of cooling the body — it made us sweat which evaporated and cooled the skin. It was too hot to work, so I declared a siesta. We found some shade and dozed off, each with his weapon close at hand.

After a few hours I knew I could not sleep for my curiosity was aroused, and so, after a few hours of tossing and turning, I gave up. I checked my pistol in its holster, took a machete and a small bag of tools, and walked back to the Junkers. I started to go over it. The two-bladed metal propeller had one tip slightly bent back, the other was undamaged.

That meant that the propeller had not been rotating on impact. I found the petrol tanks, unscrewed the caps, and dipped them with a stick stripped from a bush. Both were dry. I climbed around the aeroplane, cutting more vegetation away until I was able to inspect the entire airframe. It was not severely damaged. Apart from the propeller, the skin on the upper surface of the port wing was slightly wrinkled in two places, the skin of the fuselage on the same side was sliced neatly from behind the cabin back about a metre, and the tail skid was bent slightly sideways. One of the undercarriage legs was bent, all the others were straight, and both tyres were inflated. There was no damage to the primary structure, or at least none that I could see. There were no markings visible. Someone had taken the trouble to sand them off the sides of the fuselage and the top and bottom surfaces of the wings. The sanded areas were covered with at least two coats of black paint, under one or two coats of grey.

I heard the others approaching and called them over to help me up onto the wing root on the port side. The door was slightly ajar. Inside the cabin, just behind the pilot's seat, was a large cylindrical fuel tank. The rest of the cabin was packed full of wooden crates. The cabin had been completely stripped out. The dual controls and co-pilot's seat were gone, as were the partition between the pilots and the passengers, the passenger seats, and the lining of the cabin. The floor of the cabin had been reinforced with what looked like thick sheets of plywood. The crates were covered by a cargo net and the net was tied to rings sunk into the wooden floor. The only seat was the pilot's, on the port side. The only evidence of the pilot were brown stains, which I took to be dried blood. I found the magneto switches and saw that they were in the 'on' position. I turned them off.

The crates had rope handles and were heavy and difficult for me to lift out at such an odd angle. I took a crowbar and levered open one of the crates. Inside were twenty long bundles of waxed paper, each resting in grooves on the bottom of the crate. I unwrapped one and found myself looking at a brand-new German-made MP 28 submachine gun, still coated in the brown waxy substance called Cosmoline, which protected it from rust. I was thinking about the find when I heard a shout from about fifty metres away. Garcia had found the pilot.

He lay on his back with his left arm thrown across his face, a skeleton covered in a leather jacket, a dark brown shirt and grey trousers, and wearing leather boots and leggings like my own. A leather flying helmet, with goggles attached, lay a few metres away. I could see that the humerus, between the elbow and shoulder of his right arm, was fractured, and the femur, between the knee and hip of his right leg, was badly broken in two places. I wondered how long he had lived, knowing that he could not save himself and that no one would come to rescue him. I went through his pockets as though I searched the pockets of the dead every day. A watch with a leather strap and a broken face was on his left wrist. It had stopped at 8.17. Was it day or night? What date, I wondered? There were three pencils in his top left-hand shirt pocket: one plain, one red and one green. Some scraps of paper were scattered around, some white with indecipherable pencil marks on them and some coloured, possibly the remains of maps.

It was almost dark, so I asked the others to make camp while I had a last look at the F 13. I turned the propeller through six compressions, one for each cylinder, and found that each of them was about right. It was likely that the engine was not damaged. I opened the engine cowling without any trouble and was not surprised to find the serial number of the engine missing. The aircraft's manufacturer's identification plate should have been in the cockpit, attached to the instrument panel. There was only a square of bright metal showing where it had been prised off. No one who had gone to such trouble would pop up to claim the aeroplane. It was Paraguay's now.

As it was growing dark, I returned to the horses and camp. I dined on beef jerky with oranges and chocolate (almost liquid) for dessert. We had drawn water from the last creek we had crossed and had let the sediment settle. We now sieved it through fine cheesecloth and boiled it until we had enough to refill our water bottles and two large, rubberised canvas bags carried by one of the pack horses. We talked about our find and what we would do tomorrow. I suggested that Garcia check the airframe and engine closely and report. The night passed quietly.

* *

At first light, we had tea and hard biscuits for breakfast.

I decided to unload the aeroplane onto a level piece of ground about twenty-five metres from the crash site. There were twenty-one crates. They contained twenty MP 28s, a hundred magazines, four thousand rounds of nine-millimetre ammunition, a hundred hand grenades, and a hundred primers for the grenades.

How had the aeroplane got to the crash site? I tried to put myself in the pilot's place. This is what I knew from inspecting the plane: The cockpit had no voice radio and there were no radio navigational aids, so he was on his own the moment he was airborne. There were no blind flying instruments. No turn and slip indicator or artificial horizon or direction indicator. The petrol tanks were empty. I estimated its range as about a fifteen hundred kilometres. That meant it could have come from any of the three countries Paraguay shared borders with: Bolivia, Brazil, Argentina. Or anywhere in Uruguay and, just possibly, eastern Peru. Such a flight would have crossed large tracts of unoccupied or sparsely occupied country.

The pilot would not have set off across thousands or more kilometres of hostile terrain without a plan. Before take-off he would have drawn a line on his map, measured off the distance from his base to his destination and noted the true track. He would have known the cruising speed and fuel consumption of his aeroplane. There were no aviation weather forecasts, so he would not have known what weather he would encounter. Would the weather on his route be flyable? His only choice was to use local knowledge and run a practised eye over the sky. He would have used an estimated wind strength and direction in his calculations. The result would be a true heading, allowing for the wind, and an estimated flight time, and it would have been wise to factor in a margin for adverse winds and navigational errors.

The true heading had to be adjusted for magnetic variation and compass deviation. His map probably had the variation marked, but variation changes over time. Was the figure he used up to date and accurate? There was no compass deviation card in the cockpit. And the ferrous metal in his cargo would have produced a significant deviation from any previously calculated one. In flight, the pilot would have to rely on his compass and maps and watch to update his dead reckoning. I had not found a map, notebook, or navigation log, but the pencils and scraps of paper suggested that he had had them. Was his map accurate? His watch had stopped, but that was probably a result of the crash. It is difficult to maintain a precise heading, especially when relying solely on a compass. Assuming his knowledge of the variation and deviation were about right, but there was a 5-degree error in his compass heading, at the end of a 1,500-kilometre flight, he could be anywhere on a 150-kilometre arc. And the wind direction and strength could easily have differed from his preflight estimate. He could have been ahead or behind his estimated position on his track.

He would have had to stay clear of cloud and in sight of land or water throughout his flight. Flight over a cloud deck with no sight of the surface would have been Russian roulette. And the weather, a cold front or a warm front, would have forced him down to low altitude to try and remain in sight of the surface.

It was a mystery, but I could make an informed guess. The pilot had set off to fly a long distance over poorly mapped and inhospitable terrain with no radio or radio-navigational aids or blind flying instruments. He had become lost, had run out of fuel, and was forced to land in the thorn forest. His injuries and location made death inevitable.

There were several real mysteries — where did he come from, where was he going, and why? Who was going to use the weapons and what for? The armies of Bolivia and Paraguay had no reason to mount clandestine operations. Both nations claimed to be in the Chaco by right and did not attempt to conceal their activities. In any case, the cargo would be a drop in the bucket for armies preparing for war as there would soon be thousands of Bolivian troops in the Chaco and similar numbers of Paraguayans.

The cargo suggested some small-scale operation was in progress or at least planned. It would equip twenty men. Each would have a submachine gun and magazine, four spare magazines, two hundred rounds of ammunition, and ten grenades. Not enough for a sustained operation but enough for a raid or a coup. But who would want to mount such an operation and why? Paraguay had always been unstable. Was the shipment on its way to a group about to mount a coup? Dr Ayala expected to be elected president, and I had not heard anything about dissatisfaction with that. Still, a coup or revolution was always a possibility in Paraguay, perhaps the cargo was for one of the factions.

Several things were certain. The F 13 was in territory claimed by Paraguay, was repairable, and would be valuable to a cash-strapped nation preparing for war. Its cargo would be useful too, and it was likely that plane and cargo would be treated as Paraguayan property as of right.

Garcia reported that the engine appeared to be undamaged. There was good compression in each cylinder, the dual magnetos worked, and there was no sign of oil, water or other fluids leaking. As far as he could see, the internal structure was undamaged. I had borrowed a surveyor's tape measure and Garcia and I checked the dimensions of the aeroplane, which were identical to those in my notebook. The Junkers was 9.59 metres long, had a span of 17.75 metres, and weighed about 1,050 kilograms empty. It was not practical to move it in one piece, but it could be dismantled into three sections: port wing, starboard wing, and fuselage with tail intact. If the fuselage proved too heavy to be moved, the engine and propeller, elevators, and rudder could be unshipped.

The recovery of the Junkers would take weeks if the dismantled aeroplane had to be transported to the railhead, railed to Puerto Casado, and shipped to Asunción. If we could create an airstrip close to the crash site, things would be different. Garcia was confident that the aeroplane could be dismantled easily and repaired in a few days. With about twenty men, and block and tackle and hand tools, the aeroplane could be dismantled and loaded on wagons or sledges. If necessary, sledges could be constructed at the site using timber from a cluster of quebracho trees that grew not far away. On our way in, we had ridden through a break in the forest, bush-covered and about level, a few kilometres from the crash site. I guessed that an adequate airstrip could be created there.

The NACA technical note I had referred to was silent on take-off distances, but the Junkers was the long wing version, meaning a lighter wing loading, lower stalling speed, and shorter take-off distance. The stripped-out aeroplane, with no cargo, was light, and I would need little petrol for the flight to Casado, where the Junkers would be refuelled and flown to Ñu Guasú. There it would be fully inspected, repaired, and returned to service.

I talked it over with Garcia and we decided that we could do it. Together we came up with a plan for the recovery, repair, and return to Ñu Guasú. I wrote a dispatch with a report, diagrams, a proposed plan of action, a list of what was needed to execute it, and a request for instructions.

The Potez had a radio, but we did not, so I had arranged to use more basic forms of communication, including a message pickup. San Martin had agreed to overfly the crash site at 4 pm each day, starting today. Our campsite was in a clearing. I unpacked the necessary equipment. In the centre of the clearing, I laid out two poles, each of which telescoped to about six metres long. Attached to the tops of the poles was a loop of light rope, with one end lying on the ground. I put the message in a bag and attached the bag to the line with a snap hook. We jammed the poles into the ground about six metres apart. The line stretched between the poles, and the message bag lay on the ground. Next, I unpacked a Popham signalling panel, which could convey simple messages visually. I laid out my squares and triangles and arrows, a message in a code that the pilot would read as 'ALL OK. PICK UP MESSAGE BAG'.

Right on 4 pm, we heard the noise of an aero-engine and a Potez flew over and circled the camp twice at about sixty metres. It started to descend and straightened out when it was lined up to cross the clearing at right angles to the line connecting the poles. As it approached, I could see the message hook trailing six metres below the fuselage. The Potez swept across the clearing with its engine throttled back, the hook snagged the line, and the line snatched the bag off the ground. The pilot gave the engine full throttle and it climbed away. The aeroplane circled for a few minutes and then flew across the clearing at thirty metres. A message bag attached to a bright red streamer dropped into the clearing. I retrieved the bag. The message inside read 'RETURN TO HACIENDA AND WAIT FOR INSTRUCTIONS'.

We covered the aeroplane with brush and carefully covered the plexiglass of the cabin and cockpit windows to prevent them from glinting in the sun. I took one of the MP 28s, some spare magazines, ammunition, and ten grenades and primers and put them in my saddlebags. These were dangerous times. We covered the crates in brush. I dismantled the Popham panel and carried it back to the campsite.

Garcia and I equipped ourselves with a pick and a shovel, made one more inspection of the crash site, found nothing new, and dug a grave for the pilot. Garcia said some words over the grave, which I assumed were from the Catholic funeral rites and appropriate to the occasion. I had constructed a rough patriarchal cross, with a short cross piece and a longer one below that. Garcia carved 'INRI' into the top crosspiece.

I must have looked puzzled because he said, '*Iesus Nazarenus Rex Iudaeorum.*'

I thought back to my painfully acquired Latin and translated it out loud as 'Jesus of Nazareth, King of the Jews', and then said, 'You are assuming he was a Catholic.'

He nodded. I took the knife and with some difficulty, carved 'AN AVIATOR KNOWN ONLY TO GOD' into the longer crossbar. The wood was from a quebracho tree and will be there long after I have turned to dust.

* *

The journey back to the hacienda was easy and we waited there for several lazy days, filled with wide-ranging talk. Sandy told us about his life in the wilds of the Chaco, David cross-examined him about the flora and fauna, while Garcia and I mostly just listened, drank tea, read, and had the occasional beer.

Three days after arriving back at the hacienda, a young Lieutenant and a detachment of cavalry with their horses and equipment arrived by train. He had instructions for me. My plan had been accepted, the soldiers would assist, and teams of oxen and carts had been hired and should arrive the day after tomorrow. The command would be shared by me and the Lieutenant.

David had volunteered to help with the salvage. He said that the expedition would look well in the pages of the memoir he intended to write. Sandy found nothing urgent to do at the hacienda and joined in. He knew that the salvors of a ship received part of its value and perhaps a similar arrangement could be negotiated for the salvage of an aeroplane. The officer and I agreed to countersign Sandy's invoice but promised nothing. In a few days, all the men, animals and equipment were ready, and we decided to start the next day.

The expedition set off at dawn, led by three spans of oxen, each consisting of eight pairs yoked together and drawing a big cart with enormous wooden wheels. A tall young man, from one of the Mennonite settlements, walked alongside the first wagon, continuously shouting and cracking a whip that could reach each of the sixteen oxen. Three Indians, small in stature, with impassive faces, led the front right-hand ox in each span by a leather thong attached to the animal's horns.

The expedition made slow progress and it was three days before we arrived at the clearing. There was only one area level enough to be made suitable for take-off. One end was dominated by large, tall quebracho trees. The other had similar trees, but there was an opening about thirty metres to the right. We considered felling the trees at one end and dragging them clear, but it would have taken weeks, perhaps a month. Could I take off and clear the trees by turning right as soon as I was airborne? I estimated that a reasonably level space of 600 metres by 15 metres would be enough. Brush at the sides would have to be cut down to one metre or less for another ten metres on each side to give clearance for the wings.

The men set up camp while Garcia and I took the Lieutenant to the Junkers. We inspected the F 13 and decided that we had enough men to dismantle the aeroplane, build a sledge and load it. I estimated that the components would make up three loads. All the men and the animals would be needed to drag a loaded sledge to the clearing. The arms were where I had left them. I would have preferred that no one but those who needed to know, learn that we had found the arms. Yet rumours of a mysterious aeroplane would soon be circulating in any event. There was no way to conceal its cargo. I suggested that one-third of the crates be added to each sledge load.

First thing the next day, Garcia started the job and instructed the men. He unbolted each wing and the undercarriage from the centre section. The tailplane, elevator, and rudder were removed from the rear fuselage. The wings were light, four men could easily carry one. The fuselage was the heaviest piece, and all the men were needed. The parts of the aeroplane and the crates of arms were divided into three loads. Then a party set to work with axes, cross-cut saws, sledgehammers, wedges, and a large auger. They felled two trees, split them into rough planks, shaped them with adzes, bored holes in them, and bolted the parts together. The wood was hard, and a small treadle-operated grindstone was in regular use, resharpening the tools. Chocks, sacking for padding, and ropes kept each load in place.

The terrain between the strip and the crash site included dry watercourses, not wide but with banks three to six metres or so high. Some of them had small trees growing on their banks and we created bridges by felling many of the trees and dumping them into the obstacles. Where that was not possible, the men used pick and shovel to create ramps on each bank. There were several places where the combined efforts of the oxen had to be supplemented by men pushing the sledge while others worked with levers of roughly trimmed tree branches, levering the sledge forward a few metres at a time. At two places it took half a day to get the sledge down into the riverbed, across it, and up the other side onto level ground.

Eventually, we approached the clearing with the last load. The air had been hot and still. Clouds gathered, and the sky darkened towards the north-west. The wind rose. The cloud roiled and drifted towards us. Heat lightning crackled. The oxen and the horses became skittish. Bolts of lightning struck the ground upwind of us.

We heard the crackling first. Then clouds of smoke drifted towards us at a walking pace, spreading left and right. Flames became visible, leaping high, covering the northern horizon. If we did nothing, the sledge and its load would be consumed by flame and the remaining components would be useless. Soon we could see that the fire was advancing too fast for us to outrun it.

The Lieutenant ordered his men to set fire to the vegetation along a hundred-metre stretch downwind of the convoy to create a firebreak. As soon as our fire had burnt out an adequate area, we moved the sledge, animals, and men onto the blackened, still smoking ground. The men in charge of the animals kept them under control with great difficulty. The heat became intense, we tied cloths around our mouths, our eyes watered, our faces were scorched. All of us stamped out the remaining flames on the firebreak. I could feel the rubber soles of my boots become sticky. We choked on the thick smoke. Hundreds of birds and small animals fled from the fire, across the break.

The fire advanced toward us, paused at the edge of the firebreak, burnt along its edges and away to the south. We stood on a hot wasteland, eyes streaming, a little scorched, blackened, a few with blisters, but the aeroplane and the animals were not much the worse for wear.

Twenty minutes later, the storm broke with sheets of torrential rain. A few minutes after which it was raining so hard that we could not see more than a few metres in any direction. I have never been so pleased to be drenched to the skin. I stood with my face raised to the rain, arms out, palms open, and shouted, 'Send it down, Huey.'

It rained for the next twenty-four hours and the dry watercourses we had left behind us were full of brown water, impassable.

Back at the clearing, I conferred with the Lieutenant, and we declared a holiday until the rain stopped. We sheltered from the rain as best we could and passed around several bottles of rough cana. A drink of exceptional authority and most welcome.

* *

The weather cleared, the sky dawned clear and cool. All components were at the take-off site, so most of the men started clearing a strip for take-off while the aeroplane was reassembled, repaired, and checked over.

Garcia straightened the damaged undercarriage and reinforced it with splints of wood, wired onto each leg. He had designed and helped build a large tripod and used block and tackle and manpower to raise the fuselage off the ground so he could fit the undercarriage. Each wing, in turn, was bolted to the centre section. The tailplane, elevator, and rudder were light and were put back in place without any trouble. The tail skid was removed, straightened and reattached. Garcia had gone over the damaged panels and concluded that the damage was superficial.

When the aeroplane was in one piece, I checked that each control was connected to the stick and rudder pedals and that they moved in the correct sense. It was possible to connect a control surface with the stick or rudder pedals the wrong way around. Sometimes, men forgot to make that simple check and took off with one of the control surfaces connected in reverse. This type of error often had lethal consequences. If the ailerons were connected in that way, and a wing dropped a little soon after leaving the ground, opposite aileron made it drop further, more aileron made things worse until the aeroplane was in a steep bank, the nose dropped, and it dived into the ground killing the crew and destroying the aeroplane. The surfaces moved full and free, and in the correct sense, but with a slight binding in the ailerons. I worked my way around the aeroplane with a screwdriver, torch, and dentist's mirror on a long handle. I opened each inspection panel and checked what was behind it. I oiled each pulley, bearing and pushrod and then checked that each control surface moved smoothly. I riveted a patch over the tear in the fuselage, and my part in the repairs was done.

Meanwhile, Garcia took the propellor and, using a panel beater's bags of sand and hammers, carefully shaped the damaged propellor tip until it matched the undamaged one. He bolted the propellor back onto its hub and checked that it was secure. He checked that each magneto provided the appropriate spark. Next, he removed the spark plugs, cleaned them, and replaced them. He removed, cleaned, and reinstalled all the filters, drained the engine oil from the crankcase and filled it with fresh oil. He poured a small amount of petrol into each fuel tank and drained it, without finding any contamination.

We discussed how much petrol we should put in the fuel tanks. Too much and I might not be able to take off safely, too little I would run out before reaching Puerto Casado. Any figure would be approximate as we did not know how much fuel this engine would consume per hour, or the exact cruising speed of the aeroplane, or the winds I would encounter en route. We agreed on an amount which I estimated would cover starting and warm-up, run-up, take-off and climb, and the flight to Casado plus a fifteen-minute reserve. I helped Garcia as he strained petrol through a chamois into each of the fuel tanks, and we were ready to test the engine.

The airstrip had been cleared but the surface was a little rough and this would reduce acceleration and make the take-off run longer. I suggested that a large canvas tent be spread on the ground and loaded with rocks and soil and dragged up and down the strip. This and the hooves of the oxen would smooth out the worst imperfections.

We walked up and down the strip and found it smooth enough. The weather had been clear and windless and was unchanged. The Junkers was pushed to the back of the strip. I had decided that if the engine ran well, I would take off immediately. I checked that the wheels were chocked and that each had a rope out to the side so that they could easily be pulled away from the wheels. A soldier used a sledgehammer to drive a stake into the ground behind the tail. He tied the skid to the stake with rope and had a sharp axe at the ready.

I was flying a type of aeroplane I had never flown before. The distance I was using in my planning for take-off was an informed guess. To take off safely, I had to keep exactly straight. The cockpit was semi-enclosed, with a poor view forward. With the tail up, I would have a better view and better acceleration. If I veered only a few metres right or left of the strip, I would be in the rough ground, which would collapse the undercarriage. The machine might flip over, trapping me underneath it while petrol dripped over the hot engine. Then I had to lift off at exactly the right moment. Too soon and the Junkers would mush along and stall as soon as I tried to turn. Too late and the aircraft might be too close to the trees to turn away from them safely. If my turn was too shallow, I would hit the trees, too steep and the wingtip would dig into the ground. Any of these events would wreck the plane. I would be lucky to walk away unharmed.

There was no starter, so the engine would have to be swung into life. I sat in the cockpit and said, 'Switches off. Petrol on. Suck in.'

Garcia said, 'Switches off. Petrol on. Suck in.'

Garcia and three men linked hands and pulled the prop through six compressions. Finally, he pulled down on a tip of the prop until he could feel a compression, and said, 'Contact.'

I replied, 'Contact.'

The four men heaved together. The propellor flicked over once; the engine coughed and burst into life, producing a small cloud of oil smoke, then ran smoothly. Just like that, after who knows how long sitting out in the weather. I smiled and gave Garcia a thumbs up. He repeated the gesture. The engine instruments showed the oil pressure and temperature were rising to the appropriate levels. After a few minutes, I signalled Garcia and the others to lie across the rear fuselage and tailplane. When they were in place, I opened the throttle smoothly to almost full power and checked each magneto. One was fine but there was a 200 revolutions per minute drop on the other. Good enough. I switched back to both mags and throttled back. The men got down. Two men lay under the wings, each holding a chock rope. One was ready with the axe at the rear of the aeroplane. I signalled the men to be ready to pull the chocks away from the wheels. We had decided that I would apply full throttle, raise my arm, and then drop it. The chocks would be pulled away, the man with the axe would wait ten seconds and then chop the rope.

I pushed the throttle forward, raised my right arm, waited a few seconds, and dropped it. I held the throttle hard forward and the stick central. A lurch and the Junkers start to roll. I applied hard right rudder to keep it straight and forward pressure on the stick to raise the tail. The airspeed indicator needle did not move. I would have to judge the take-off by feel. The tail came up, I eased off a little of the right rudder to keep straight, felt the aircraft become buoyant, and lifted it off the ground. It rose to about ten metres and turned gently to the right. The left wingtip cleared the trees by a few metres.

* *

As soon as I was clear I eased the power back and flew due north, climbing to about 600 metres. I picked up a stream, following it due east to the Rio Paraguay. I followed the Paraguay south. The oil pressure and temperatures were normal, and the engine ran smoothly, which was a relief because there was nowhere to land safely if the engine gave up the ghost.

After about thirty minutes, the factory at Puerto Casado came into sight and then the airstrip. I flew overhead and noted that the wind was calm and there was no air traffic. I landed and taxied up to the headquarters. I cut the engine, the propellor slowed, flicked around one last time, and stopped. A small crowd gathered and Estigarribia emerged from his headquarters, smiling. I climbed down and said, 'I would like to refuel and head down to Asunción first thing in the morning.'

He said, 'Agreed. Come inside and find me when you are finished.'

A competent-looking NCO in Air Force uniform came over and told me he had been ordered to supervise the refuelling. I said, 'I took off with only an hour's fuel to save weight and shorten the take-off distance. Please strain the petrol through a chamois leather and fill both tanks to the brim. Better fill the tank in the cabin, as well.'

He replied, 'Of course.'

Refuelling was from a stack of twenty-litre tins. A soldier sat on the wing, opened the cap on the fuel tank and insert a funnel. The top end of the funnel was covered with a chamois. Some soldiers opened the tins and passed them up. When that tank was full, the same method was used to fill the tank in the other wing, and the long-range tank in the cabin.

Soon I was in Colonel Estigarribia's office. There was no guard at the door, which was closed, and I was sitting in a comfortable cane armchair, drinking Earl Grey tea. This was a great improvement on my first experience of being interviewed in Paraguay. No Pyragues, black suits or black car.

We exchanged pleasantries. He said, 'Let's go for a walk.'

He stood, put his cap on, and we walked through the anteroom where the soldiers, typists, and clerks, stood at attention, respectfully but not rigidly. We walked to the riverbank, or as close to it as the inundations allowed.

Estigarribia said, 'Tell me about this mystery aeroplane.'

I explained about the absence of markings and the missing constructor's identification plates on the engine and airframe, the cargo of arms, and my theory of how it got to the crash site.

He asked, 'Where are the arms?'

'Your soldiers are on their way here with them. They will probably arrive in about four days. I have one of the MP 28s and some of the ammunition.'

Anywhere else in the world my confession would have raised eyebrows, but this was Paraguay. In the 1930s. All he said was, 'Well, these are uncertain times. I will keep the rest here. You never know when they might be useful. Do you have a theory about all this? I mean, where did it come from, why did it come down in the Chaco, and who were these weapons for?'

I explained my theory that it could have come from anywhere within at least fifteen hundred kilometres, and that the pilot was almost certainly lost. I added that the arms suggested a raid or a coup. Estigarribia followed my explanation and clearly understood the technical parts of it. He said, 'I agree. Let us wait and see what happens.'

We stood in silence, watching as a sidewheel steamer pulled away from the wharf, leaving a thick trail of wood smoke, almost vertical, in the still air, and a double wake of muddy, disturbed water behind the paddle wheels.

Estigarribia said, 'Not a very pretty river, is it?'

'No, it is not.'

He went on, 'In the next few weeks, we are sending you on a trip to evaluate some aircraft we have been offered in Argentina and Uruguay. I would like you to keep your eyes and ears open. You may encounter Bolivians, possibly one or two Bolivian diplomats or military officers who are attached to the Bolivian Embassy in Buenos Aires. You will be briefed before you go. If there is no contact, no problem. It is just a thought. If you do make contact, we would like you to hint that you can supply Bolivia with valuable information. How would you like to do that?'

This was a surprise. Not so long ago I was suspected of being a spy, now I was being asked to be a spy. This approach suggested that I was now perceived as trustworthy. Estigarribia was only a Lieutenant-Colonel, commanding a regiment of infantry at an outpost remote from the halls of power. This was only the latest clue that there was an informal command structure, parallel to, and at least as powerful as, the formal one.

'What would I have to do?'

'Officially, you would be on a buying trip, finding and evaluating aircraft for the Aviación en Campaña. Your story will be explained to you by Intelligence, as will ways and means. You will tell no one what you are doing. Your cover will be good. Most of it will be true, always a good thing in this type of operation.'

'Why me?'

'You work for the Air Force in a position of trust. You are gaining a reputation as a skilled and resourceful man. You are a foreigner, and they are likely to assume that you have no loyalty and are corruptible. Well?'

It sounded exciting. Dangerous. A new experience. I said, 'I will do it.'

We had walked along a path back through the bush and were on the boundary of the airfield. I said, 'Almost everything I know, the Bolivians can learn from any one of half a dozen aviation journals and the newspapers here and abroad.'

'They can, but every little bit of information you can give them reinforces your cover story. At the very least it will persuade them that you have a technical turn of mind and have a good memory. You will have insights into the operation and handling of aeroplanes that are not in the journals. This will interest them, without revealing anything of great value to them.'

'I see. What I do know is just a tease, isn't it?'

'It is.'

He took a folded piece of paper from his tunic pocket and handed it to me. 'This the name and home telephone number of your contact in

Asunción. All meetings will be at his home or some other suitable civilian location.'

He took out a leather cigar case, took one out, offered me one and lit both, but did not extinguish his match. 'Have you memorised the name and number?'

I said, 'Yes.'

He took the paper from me, set it alight, dropped the ashes, and ground them into the dirt with his heel. 'This may seem a little melodramatic, but this kind of thing needs to be done right or not at all. So, it is settled.'

He paused and then went on, 'Do you know how I became a soldier?'

'I don't.'

'It happened in 1908. I had just finished my studies in agronomy and would have lived out my life advising farmers, except I was walking through Asunción looking for a café when I saw armed men, in uniform. There was a revolution taking place. I volunteered, my side won, and in 1910, I was rewarded with a commission in the infantry. Soldiering suited me. I was on the winning side in several revolutions, survived serious wounds, and was sent to study at the Chilean Army's Academia de Guerra in Santiago. I fought on the winning side in the Civil War of 1922 to 1923 and studied at the French Army's École Supérieure de Guerre in Paris.

'Bolivia is our enemy, of course. In 1908, Bolivia decided to modernise its Army and Germany sent a mission headed by Major Hans Kundt. In 1911, he began reorganising the Bolivian Army on the Prussian model. By all accounts, he was an excellent administrator and instructor. When the Great War started in 1914, Kundt returned home, served in combat posts throughout the war and rose to the rank of General. He returned to Bolivia after the armistice and continued reorganising the Army. Eventually, he was given the rank of General and appointed Chief of Staff of the Army and Minister of War of Bolivia. He was both efficient and popular. In 1930, President Hernando Siles Reyes was deposed in a coup. Kundt was identified as an ally of Siles and was exiled. I studied his Great War career when I was at the Ecole Supérieure. He believed in vigorous use of the telephone and repeated frontal attacks. He has been sacked, but he might return. We think that he knows little or nothing about the Chaco and his tactics are costly in the lives of his soldiers. If we must fight, I hope Kundt is in command.'

In the morning, it rained heavily, there was low cloud, and the visibility was less than five hundred metres. I remained grounded. Late that afternoon the weather changed, and the sky was clear. With full petrol tanks and an engine that ran smoothly, I had no concerns. Before I reached Asunción, I turned east and then back south-west to avoid flying over the city. The working day at the airfield was finished by the time I arrived, and the only people around were some soldiers. I had them help me and soon the Junkers was in the hangar, pushed into the back corner with the crates of books. It was covered in dust sheets and would have to wait until I had the time to assess what needed to be done. The soldiers were from an infantry regiment and showed no interest in the F 13. I had an idea that it could be fitted out for several roles. Seats for passengers, stretchers for sick or wounded, and tie-down points for cargo. If we could find some bomb racks, the aeroplane could be used as a bomber.

As soon as the Junkers was safely in the hangar, I phoned my contact who was a Major in the Army Engineers. I had expected him to be assigned to Army Intelligence and was puzzled by this, as I was puzzled by this whole game. However, the Major impressed me with his competence and intelligence and by his clarity of thinking.

At my second meeting with the Major, in the study of his home, we talked about how to get the Bolivians interested in me, without hinting that it was a setup. The Major said, 'There are cafés and bars where some of the Bolivian Embassy staff socialise. If you become a regular and are on your own, it would be natural for them to strike up a conversation. You play poker and bridge?'

'Yes.'

'The Bolivian Military Attaché in Buenos Aires plays poker, seriously. And he is an aviator. The embassy operates a light aeroplane; he flies it, and he is learning to fly gliders. There is only one main airfield, and your business will take you there. Poker and flying may be an in. You can talk freely about your cover, buying aeroplanes, but not prices or too much detail. They will not value information that they get for nothing. And they need to think they are seducing you. Do aviators love talking shop?'

'They do.'

'So, you play poker and talk flying. In due course, you can hint that you are unhappy with your employers. Do not overdo it. You will probably have to improvise.'

'It is likely that I will not make a connection.'

'That is not a problem. Anyway, you have to be in BA, perhaps you need to visit it again. Just keep your eyes and ears open.'

For telegrams, I was to use a code based on a book. Each of us would have a copy of the same edition of the same book, and it had to be a title that would not seem out of place in my possession. We settled on a cheap edition of the *King James Bible* in English.

The Major said, 'Have you practised encoding and decoding using the book method, as we discussed?'

'I have. Here is a sample.'

I watched while the Major decoded it. He smiled. 'The text of our national anthem?'

I smiled back, 'I am starting to feel a little Paraguayan.'

We had concluded that my activities must be consistent with my cover, a civilian employee of the Arma Aérea Paraguaya on assignment in

Argentina and Uruguay to locate and assess available aeroplanes and negotiate their purchase.

We finalised the plan. When I departed for Buenos Aires by ship, I was to be gregarious, friendly, and talkative. On the ship and in my first days in Argentina, I should give no hint of dissatisfaction with my employers. I should dress neatly, but not expensively, like a civil servant on a modest salary. If I was bought a drink, I should shout the next round but not shout the bar. I would book into the cheapest room at one of the best hotels. Just as a minor official with ambitions might.

If there was a card game on offer, I could join in and play as well as I could. Coded telegrams could plausibly be explained as routine reports of my search for aeroplanes and negotiations for their purchase. If I was noticed sending them, it might enhance my cover as a man who knew things.

The Major said, 'Excellent. Good luck. If they bite, ask for gold. They will only value what they pay for. Whatever amount they offer you, ask for twice as much.' He paused and went on, 'There may be opportunities we have not thought of, be ready to exploit them.'

Chapter Eight
A Noiseless Wing. 21 March 1932

When he finds a piece of air that is going up, the pilot naturally wishes to stay in it. If it is going up because it is surmounting a hill, he flies up and down along the crest of the hill. If it is thermal lift, it will probably take the form of air rising in a column or bubble, which drifts along with the wind.
— Robert Kronfeld. *Kronfeld on Gliding and Soaring: The Story of Motorless Human Flight.* 1932

The Stratus is a two-seat glider designed for training and soaring in ridge lift and thermals. The instruments, seat belts, metal fittings, cables, wires, pulleys, and pushrods are available from the manufacturer for a modest price. A small group of skilled woodworkers should be able to complete construction in six months of evenings and weekends.
— *Gliding Magazine.* 3 November 1931

Sailplanes are not silent, but they are quiet and the cockpit in the nose gives a panoramic view of unparalleled beauty, one that the gods might envy. Garcia and his men had almost finished their glider, the first in Paraguay, and the thought of soaring, wresting altitude, distance, and speed from the invisible forces of nature, was tantalising.

I had flown gliders before, in Germany, during a leave from the RAF in 1928. I learned to glide and to soar on the dunes of Rossitten in East Prussia with the Rhön-Rossitten Gesellschaft. My photographs from that holiday are in front of me now. Fit, tanned young men and women watching graceful gliders soaring over the white sand dunes overlooking the Kurisches Haff.

The result of the thousands of hours of skilled work shaping and tacking or glueing into place more than ten thousand pieces of wood, was a simple but graceful machine that would carry a pilot and pupil in open cockpits set in tandem under and in front of the high wing. The undercarriage consisted of a single wheel and a skid, so the glider rested on the wheel and a wingtip when it was stationary on the ground.

Each cockpit had a plywood seat, a seatbelt, a stick, rudder pedals, a red-painted handle that operated the tow release, and a few simple instruments.

Now was the time to test our creation. The launch required the carefully co-ordinated efforts of at least four people. A remarkable number of things can go wrong in aviation operations, and everybody involved in the test flights had received a thorough briefing in front of the blackboard, and again just before the launch.

A truck with a winch attached was in place on the far side of the airfield, with the winch operator seated facing the launch site. A wire from the drum of the winch was laid out on the airfield with its end in front of the glider. Beside the glider, there was a man equipped with a large paddle — a disc on a stick, painted bright red.

I sat in the open front cockpit, with only a small semi-circle of plexiglass between me and the slipstream; the rear cockpit was empty. An assistant hooked the wire into the release and held it taut. I pulled the release to check it and then had it hooked on again. I instructed the wingtip man to hold the wings level. Then I said, 'Take up slack.' The wingman waved the paddle left and right, underarm, and the cable was reeled in until all the slack was gone. I said, 'All-out.' At the wingtip, the helper raised his arm above his head and waved the paddle back and forth in a wide arc.

The winch driver let out the clutch and smoothly opened the throttle. The glider moved forward. I could feel the controls becoming effective as we accelerated. The man ran alongside, supporting the wingtip. I left him behind and held the wings level with the ailerons. When I had flying speed, I eased the stick back and held the glider in a steep climb, the airspeed stabilised, the ground fell away, the sensation was exhilarating. Soon the glider was at the top of the climb, I eased forward on the stick, pulled the release knob, the rope dropped away, and the glider was flying free.

I was at an altitude of about 500 metres, and I had about ten minutes to check the handling and simultaneously plan my approach. I turned smoothly left and right, eased the nose up and checked the low-speed handling, stalled, and recovered, and then it was time to land. There was just enough height to safely turn at right angles to the landing strip and then on to final approach. The ground came up to meet me and I eased back on the stick until I was flying parallel to the ground at an altitude of one metre, and the glider touched smoothly. It slid along on its skid and wheel, came to a halt, and gently settled onto its left wingtip.

By the time I had undone my harness and climbed out, I was surrounded by smiling men. Their beautiful creation flew. They insisted on shaking my hand and clapping me on the back.

This was 1932, and there was no one to insist on a long programme of test flights or formal certification. I had confidence in the designer and builders. The glider felt right, so after one more brief test flight, I embarked on the task of teaching my colleagues to fly.

We were blessed by fine weather seven days in a row, and each day at dawn before the Air Force started flying, we flew our glider. All of the men showed some aptitude for piloting. By the end of the week, I was able to send two men solo and saw the glider in the air for the first time. I watched them with the trepidation common to all instructors watching first solo flights.

Part of my agreement with the mechanics was that after they had all had some flights, I was free to take the glider on holiday with me. I arranged ten days' leave, and Sophia and I drove north-east into the countryside, towing the dismantled glider on a simple trailer, looking for suitable launch sites. Over the last few months, I had looked for them when flying and marked them on my map. One of the sites was perfect: long, high and at right angles to the prevailing wind.

Sophia had been out of town during the week I had been flying the glider and had not even seen the glider rigged for flight. We were driving into the hills with Sophia regaling me with the eccentricities and sexual preferences of some of the teachers at the Bauhaus, when she suddenly changed direction and said, 'How will you get into the air?'

'We will rig the glider at the top of a line of hills and line up into the wind and be catapulted into the air with a bungy.'

'What is a bungy?'

'It is a V-shaped rubber cord, about sixty metres long on each side. A ring in the apex of the V fits into a hook in the nose. A team of men stretch the bungy out. One man holds the tail. When I say "Release", the cord catapults the glider forward and up to flying speed and into the air.'

'Then what?'

'If there is no lift, we will glide down to the bottom of the hill and land. We won't need much room for that, a small field will be enough. If there is sufficient wind, we will soar, stay aloft and climb up into the sky.'

'How will you make your glider soar?'

'By finding lift, an air mass going up at a greater rate than the glider is going down.' I explained ridge lift and thermals, and how to get the best out of the glider. 'The rate of climb depends on the conditions and the skill of the pilot. It is essential to fly smoothly, co-ordinating the controls so you are not slipping or skidding. If the flying is clumsy, the glider does not display its best performance.'

'How far can you glide when there is no lift?'

'I think our machine has a glide angle of about eighteen to one. That is, eighteen metres forward for each one metre down.'

I expanded what I had said about ridge lift. 'Imagine a rock in a stream, one that just breaks the surface. You will see the water flow up the rock and down the other side. The air does that, only on a much greater scale. The strength of the lift depends mainly on the shape and height of the hill. Also, on the direction and strength of the wind. A pilot learns to know where to go to get the best lift. And where not to go.'

'Where not to go?'

'If you are ridge soaring, there is lift in front of the hill but behind it, the air is flowing downwards, and sometimes it is also rolling over and over, very turbulent and dangerous.'

'How far can you soar? How high?'

'Imagine your line of hills is thirty kilometres long, and the wind strength and direction are the same all along it, and there are no gaps, then you can soar the thirty kilometres. And back if you want to. If there is a gap, but you are skilful, you may have enough height to glide across it and soar on. How high, depends on conditions and skill. Routinely, you can climb to anything between a hundred and fifty metres and six hundred metres on a good hill in a strong wind. You can stay in the air as long as the wind blows. Duration flights are good for a pilot to gain experience in the air, develop skills. Then there are the thermals I told you about. Often the thermals are marked by cumulus clouds. You can fly cross-country by climbing in one thermal, then glide to the next, circle in it, and repeat for as long as you can. In Europe, there have been flights of over a hundred kilometres. And that is only the beginning. I predict that pilots will fly further and higher and there is no practical limit. Some pilots are experimenting with finding and using other sources of lift. Soaring in wave lift is being developed. I would need a blackboard to explain that one.'

We arrived at the ridge I had spotted from the air, parked the trailer, and went looking for men to help us rig and launch. Sophia negotiated with some peasant farmers who spoke only Guarani. She offered them a modest fee for their assistance, and it was accepted.

In my experience, farmers can turn their hands to almost anything and they made quick work of extracting the glider from the trailer. They laid the sections on the grass, left and right wings, fuselage, tailplane, elevator and four struts, two on each side to brace the wing against the fuselage. When the glider was rigged, I pegged it down and briefed the farmers. We did several dummy launches until I was sure they knew what to do.

I checked the controls for full and free movement and the three instruments: an airspeed indicator, an altimeter, and a variometer. The variometer consisted of two vertical tubes, one with a red pellet in it and one with a green pellet. If the glider was descending, the red pellet rose, and if it was rising, the green pellet rose.

I could see a field at the bottom of the ridge that was big enough to land in if the lift was inadequate. We rested pointing into the wind. The breeze was strong and steady. I had flown the glider at least seventy times, and now we would find out how well it soared. Sophia was in the back cockpit. Sixteen farmers had been briefed to stretch the bungy, eight on each side of the V. Another man held the wings level, and one was behind the glider, holding a rope connected to the tail skid. I shouted, in Guarani, the only three words I knew. 'Walk.' They walked forward and out to each side, stretching the bungy. 'Run.' They ran and disappeared over the crest. 'Release.' The tail man let go and we were smoothly catapulted into the air.

Almost immediately I felt the surge upwards conferred by the air flowing up the slope. The green pellet of the variometer rose, showing that we were climbing. I kept the wings level and the nose slightly down. Forward of the ridge, the rate of climb fell off and I turned parallel to the slope to stay within the area of the lift, then turned slightly into the wind so that we did not drift back into the rough air descending in the lee of the ridge. The invisible air was not smooth, and we were shaken by small gusts and eddies. Crabbing along the ridge, I explored the invisible region of rising air. As we gained height the wind speed increased, and I had to increase the crab angle until it was at forty-five degrees to the windward side of the ridge. We rose to about 300 metres above the ridge, about 450 metres above the field at its base.

As we climbed the hills, farms and forests were spread out below us. The air was unusually clear, and I could just see the Rio Paraguay, many kilometres to the west.

The slipstream hissed quietly around us, and I chatted with Sophia, explaining what I was doing. Then I asked her if she would like to fly the glider.

'Yes, very much.'

I said, 'Right hand on stick and feet on rudders, lightly, as I showed you on the ground. I will follow through. Keep the nose below the horizon with the elevator and the wings level with the ailerons.' There was a little wobble or two but soon I could take my hands and feet off the stick and the rudder pedals. We started to drift back towards the ridge. I said, 'Bank left a little. That's it. Straighten out, wings level.'

The ridge was about five kilometres long and we were about to reach the end, where the wind was going around the hill, rather than over it. The lift was consequently decreasing, and the air became more turbulent. I said, 'We are going to turn left and crab back along to the launch site. Follow me through.' I turned away from the ridge and established us crabbing back along it. I guessed that at this altitude, the lift might be stronger further forward of the ridge. I said, 'Lower the nose, we will pick up speed and move forward, further away from the ridge.'

The wind speed increased and so did the lift. We soared higher and higher. A greater and greater crab angle was necessary until we were pointing directly into the wind, the wind speed matching our airspeed, and we hovered motionless, save for the occasional disturbance in the air. I held my hands up to show Sophia that she had control. She said, 'I could stay here forever.'

I said, 'So could I.' I paused, then added, 'This quiet sail is as a noiseless wing, to waft me from distraction.'

Sophia said, 'That is lovely, but I don't think it is original.' I confessed that it was from *Childe Harold's Pilgrimage* by Lord Byron.

We did three launches that afternoon and spent over three hours in the air. Sophia spent more than half of that at the controls.

* *

That night we camped by a small lake of clear water, with a fast-flowing stream to cool the wine. The adventure, the magic of flight (and a little wine), created a mellow yet alert state of mind. Sophia dared me to come swimming au naturel. The water was cold but sensual, erotic. I saw her naked and unselfconscious, the nipples on her small breasts hard, her clump of pubic hair dark against her fair skin. We stood facing each other, she held me against her.

Afterwards, skin to skin, wrapped in a blanket, lying close to the fire, she traced my scars with the tip of a finger. She had done that before but never asked about them. She touched my nose. 'How did you break it? I've been meaning to ask.'

'It is a Siskin nose.'

'What?'

'Siskin nose. One of the fighters I flew in the RAF was the Armstrong Whitworth Siskin IIIA. An odd-looking machine, a sesquiplane, one-and-a-half wings. A full-size upper wing and a vestigial lower wing. It has some quirky and dangerous characteristics. If you land crosswind, or there is a gusty wind, and don't get it perfectly right, they are prone to dropping a wing. One day it was gusty, I was tired, a wing dropped, dug into the ground, and the aeroplane went over on its back. I was thrown forward onto the front of the cockpit coaming and broke my nose. It happens so often to Siskin pilots that the injury has a name. It happened twice.'

She smiled and said, 'Are you sure it was not a Mark IV?' She knew little about aeroplanes, this was just her teasing me about being unnecessarily precise. She went on, 'Tell me about the second time.'

She was asking about the flight that I had thought about during my interrogation by Arturo Bray. 'I spent a year flying in the Meteorological Flight at Duxford. We did climbs to six thousand metres or seven thousand five hundred metres twice a day, six days a week. In an open cockpit and with basic instruments and no radio or radio navigation aids. We did have electrically heated flying suits and oxygen. The purpose was to note air pressure and temperature and the types of clouds and their altitudes. This was for weather forecasting. We telephoned the Weather Office in London after landing and gave them the figures and observations. Anyway, the weather was often bad but that did not stop us. One day I was descending through solid cloud and hoping to find the cloud base a few hundred metres above the ground, but it was not to be. The cloud took on a greenish tinge, and I slammed into the ground, collapsing the undercarriage. I opened the throttle, staggered over a hedge, chopped the throttle. The Siskin flopped down, the damaged undercarriage dug in, and the aeroplane cartwheeled. I broke my nose on the cockpit coaming. Again.'

She put her hand on my torso and left thigh, running her fingertips over the scars. She said, 'And these?'

I thought about the question and said, 'Flying, in peace and war.'

She touched the deep scars on my upper right arm. 'They look deliberate?'

I had nightmares about the day I acquired them. All I said was, 'A misunderstanding.'

She looked at me. 'Wouldn't it be safer to stick to lawyering? I mean, you might live longer.'

I laughed; she was right. But I was never going to give up going in harm's way. I could not explain the attraction of danger in its many forms, the hazards of flying in bad weather, operating poorly maintained aeroplanes from inadequate airstrips. Air combat was the most exciting of all. Proving myself to myself, the feeling of being competent, authentic. I missed the Great War. My brother did not. He flew and fought and told me about it — fear, excitement, validation.

Soon, I would acquire more scars and the stories that went with them.

I changed the subject and said, 'What makes you happy?'

'An accumulation of small pleasures. You must be alert and recognise the opportunities. And don't expect too much of them.'

She was silent for a few seconds, then said, 'I find that saying yes to every opportunity for happiness works. Like taking my dress off for a man I had known less than two days.'

'But I did not ask you to.'

'No, but you would have, that evening, the day after. I just advanced the process. I wanted you, I guessed that you wanted me. I was right, wasn't I?'

'Yes, very much so.'

She said, 'You are self-assured around women.'

'I discovered, a long time ago, that if I did not try hard, was relaxed, I was more likely to attract a woman.'

Sophia pushed me onto my back and straddled me. She said, 'You are very beautiful. Even your scars.' She ran her fingertips lightly over my forehead, face, neck, and chest. She moved back until she was sitting on my thighs. Her fingertips explored all that she could see of me.

Afterwards, we gathered more firewood and built the fire up. The air was crisp and clean and cool. We lay there silent for a while, and then we talked about intimacies and why we are fond of or love a person. I gave an example, my baby sister. 'When she left home to go to teachers college in Christchurch, aged seventeen, she left her soft toys on her bed, arranged as she had arranged them since she was a little girl. She is a grown-up now, a teacher, and married with children, yet I often think of her as that seventeen-year-old girl.'

Sophia talked about her mother. Her mother worked hard, day after day, poor, proud, keeping the cottage scrupulously clean and putting food on the table. And entering into the arrangement with the landowner's son and yet retaining her dignity. All of these things, examples that Sophia would never forget or cease to be proud of. The conversation turned to the creative parts of our lives. She said, 'Do you like the house I am designing for you?'

'I do and I like the process.'

The next day dawned still and hot. We had left the glider tied down on the hill and had agreed to pay one of our helpers if it was intact when we returned. We rested in the shade of the upturned wing while we waited for the right conditions. I suggested that Sophia occupy the front seat and do as much of the flying as she could, and she agreed. She was much lighter than me, so I got some canvas bags of lead shot from the trailer and put them in the locker under the front seat to make up the difference and keep the centre of gravity in the right place. Just before midday, a breeze arrived and quickly gathered strength. We fetched our launch crew and were bungeed off into the slope lift and tacked back and forward over our launch site.

The ridge and the slope leading up towards it was covered in long grass that undulated like the sea as the wind passed over it. After about twenty minutes in the air, I could see that a section of the grass was being disturbed by something other than the wind. It was as if the wind in the section was being whirled around and around and it was moving up the hill. It was a thermal. If I turned towards the thermal and circled in it, I could rise above the slope lift. I gently turned a little left and right to time my arrival opposite the thermal at the correct moment, and then turned directly away from the slope and into the thermal. The glider surged upwards, and the rate of climb increased smoothly as I approached the core of the thermal. To stay in it, I would have to circle, but if I circled in the wrong direction, I would fly out of it. I guessed that left was the correct direction and rolled quickly towards it. I had guessed right. Immediately we were climbing rapidly with the green pellet in the variometer high up in its tube, at about 500 metres per minute.

The ground fell away and soon the glider was at 1,000 metres. I could see many kilometres in every direction through the clear air. The column of air I was circling in was travelling south-east, away from the ridge, at the speed of the wind, about thirty-five kilometres per hour. I would soon have to decide whether to return to the slope or cut myself free and go across country. To return to the slope, I would have to leave the thermal and its lift and enter a descending glide into the wind. Gliding into the wind, the ground speed and glide angle would be halved. Gliding downwind, the ground speed and glide angle would be enhanced.

I could see scattered cumulus clouds, each marking the top of a thermal. I decided to leave the ridge, and straightened out and flew south-east, downwind and away from it. We flew out of the lift and the green pellet sank to the bottom of its tube and the red pellet rose. We were covering the ground at the rate of about thirty metres forward for every one metre of altitude lost. I estimated that we had about ten to fifteen minutes to find and centre in a thermal. If not, I would have to find a field, plan an approach and land. There were fields, but not many and all of them small.

I need not have worried, as we were soon in another thermal and climbing at 300 metres per minute. The cloud base was rising, the lift was getting stronger, and the clouds marking the tops of the thermals were closer together. The wind veered slowly around from north-west to due north, and I turned south to get the maximum benefit from the tailwind. Sophia knew that I had to concentrate, and she sat quietly to let me get on with it. I explained what I was doing and had her fly when we were established in a thermal and when gliding straight toward the next one. We were now flying over the settled areas near the Ferrocarril Central del Paraguay and there was no shortage of fields to land in.

The day turned into the evening and the thermals died down and the air became smooth. We glided due south giving up altitude for distance.

I saw the railway and puffs of smoke from a wood-fired locomotive as it approached a station. I now had a choice of fields and I picked one close to the station. We arrived overhead with at least 1,000 metres to spare. I pushed the nose down until we were in a steep descent and the airspeed indicator was pegged against the stop. The slipstream howled past us. I pulled up until the glider was in a vertical climb, the speed falling off. Just before we stalled, I let the nose drop and rolled into a right-hand turn, reversing direction and diving back towards the field. I pulled up smoothly, regaining some of the height I had lost, bleeding off the airspeed until it was down to approach speed, a safe margin above the stall.

The train was now standing in the station and the smoke from its stack showed that there was a light wind from the west. I turned downwind, then base leg, and then on to final approach, judging that I would have ten metres to spare as I passed over a hedge on the downwind side. Keeping the nose below the horizon, I slide-slipped the excess height away, straightened out, rolled the wings level, and eased the stick back to flatten out. I felt and heard the wheel as we touched and ran along the ground, losing speed. Easing the stick forward a little put the skid on the ground and the friction slowed us to a halt. We stopped and the left wing dropped gently to the ground.

The only noise was the distant chuffing of the locomotive and we said nothing for some seconds, savouring our experience and achievement.

Chapter Nine
SS *Miranda*. 10 April 1932

The steamers in the Buenos Aires–Asunción service leave Buenos Aires on Sundays and Thursdays and Asunción on the same days. Accommodations are very comfortable, and in general, the trip is one of the most pleasant that can be made in South America.

– US Department of Commerce. Paraguay, A Commercial Handbook. 1920

'The flower of a generation of young men are buried on the banks of these rivers, countless Paraguayans, Brazilians, Uruguayans, and Argentinians.' The speaker was Max Weber, historian, bon vivant, merchant of death, and racist.

Our ship was sailing downstream along a horseshoe bend in the Rio Paraguay, just before it merges with the Rio Parana. He had been talking almost continuously since our ship left Asunción. He was passionate about the history of the War of the 70 of 1864 to 1870, and he assumed everyone else was. He pointed to the ruins of the Fortress of Humaitá, once described as the Gibraltar of South America, but now a low series of what had once been entrenchments, shell-proof shelters, and revetments for artillery. The only building visible was the ruins of the Church of San Carlos Borromeo.

Max continued, 'The geography of the position forced the Brazilian fleet to pass within two hundred metres of the Paraguayan artillery and there was a massive boom supporting an iron chain. The river was sown with fixed and floating mines. The minefield was covered by artillery, so it could not be swept, and the land approaches to the fortress were marsh that could not be traversed by large bodies of men, or at least not men under fire. Massed Paraguayan infantry and artillery were well protected. It took a year or so to force a passage past and compel the surviving Paraguayans to withdraw. Or have you heard the story?'

I smiled and said, 'Some of it.'

Max was short and stout, with a gin-drinker's nose and dressed in a rumpled off-white linen suit. For all the world he looked like an actor in a B-movie playing an Old China Hand. I had seen plenty of the real thing in China. He was open about what he was and what he did, he was a merchant of death, specifically, he sold arms for Vickers-Armstrongs Limited of Great Britain, everything from belt buckles to battleships. He had been trying to sell arms to Paraguay. This was surprising for two reasons. I had heard whispers that over the past five or six years, Paraguay had spent a large proportion of its annual revenues on rearmament, from Argentinian cavalry saddles and Italian gunboats to French bomber and fighter aircraft. The national treasury was empty, or nearly so. The other cause for puzzlement was that Max's employer was supplying a large range of arms to Bolivia, including tanks, flame-throwers, and combat aeroplanes. Max was relaxed about the notion of arming both sides in a build-up to what was likely to be a war, and he had said, 'If the niggers want to fight, why should I ignore an opportunity?'

That kind of language and thinking was common amongst those who considered themselves white men. Max had a deeply held contempt for anybody and any nation that did not speak English and whose inhabitants did not have white skins. He had lived in South America long enough to be fluent in Spanish, but without acquiring any great insights into the people's values. If he respected anything about the societies that had made him welcome, he gave no indication of it. If they wanted to kill each other, well, it was not up to him to prevent them from doing so.

The discussion turned to aeroplanes and Max quickly work out that I was an aviator. He talked about his employer's aircraft and then he smoothly directed the conversation to Paraguayan aviation. He was full of questions, and I answered some of them with information that was freely available in journals and newspapers. I told him I could not answer his other questions because civilian employees were not privy to such information. A few drinks later, and after I had hinted that I might know more, I steered the conversation to the bars and brothels of Asunción, a topic of great interest to him.

Father de Morais broke into the conversation and picked up on another topic we had been talking about. 'Paraguay is part of the Anglican Diocese of the Falkland Islands.'

Max and de Morais had both found out that I was interested in many things and was usually a good listener.

Father de Morais paused and drank his tall glass of iced beer in one draught. I had lost count of the number of glasses of iced beer he had drunk, and I was a bit hazy about how many I had consumed. Father Venancio de Morais had earned those beers and many future ones, for he ran a mission station in the Chaco, somewhere south-west of Bahia Negra, far from any railway, road, or track, and rich in heat, dust, disease, hostile fauna, and Indians. If I remember correctly, he was a member of a German religious order, The Missionary Oblates of Mary Immaculate, and the mission station was established to evangelise the indigenous peoples.

The first few days of my nascent career as a spy had started so pleasantly that I had to remind myself that I had a job to do. And so, on the way to being a spy, I was indulging my love of history and an unquenchable thirst for knowledge, in the company of a learned priest and an arms salesman.

Father de Morais was a tallish, thin man with black hair and a fair complexion. He was dressed in mufti, a shabby black jacket and worn moleskin trousers. When I asked him why he was not dressed like a priest, he told me that it felt more like a holiday if he left formal wear behind. He was personable, well read, and a fount of information about religion in this part of the world. I had been increasing my meagre knowledge of the subject for the past few hours. Before today, all I had known was that most Paraguayans professed the Catholic faith, that some of the men and women who had settled in Paraguay over the last fifty years were Protestant, and that Asunción seemed to have many fine churches. Plus, that there were uncounted Indians whose spiritual beliefs were known only to a few scholars. My ecclesiastical friend was remarkably objective about how much he could achieve with peoples whose contact with white men had been largely negative. The white men, for want of a better term, that the Indians had encountered did not see them as human and had frequently raped or murdered them. On the other hand, many white men who had ventured into the Indians' territories had failed to return to civilisation, and not all of them had died of thirst or snakebite.

I asked, 'How many tribes are there in the Chaco?'

'Depends on how you define a tribe, sixteen or seventeen, maybe more. There are five families of languages and many variations on each. The area is largely unexplored, in my bailiwick the Matacoco tribe predominates. The General, Juan Belaieff, is systematically exploring and studying the Indians, their cultures, and languages.'

I said, 'I have met the General. The old boy is an interesting man. Most ex-Czarist officers are only interested in vodka, cards, and women. Belaieff is a Renaissance man. Ethnographer, explorer, linguist, and something of an expert on artillery and military engineering. And a first-class host.'

'He is. Have you been to his home? It contains a wonderful collection of native art.'

'I have and it does. And he keeps a good table.'

The Father looked puzzled, and I realised that the expression did not translate well and sounded like a comment on the quality of his furniture. I said, 'Sorry. I mean that his guests are interesting people with a fascinating range of interests and accomplishments.'

'Aah, yes.'

The Father intended to spend his leave enjoying the civilised delights of Argentina. He was good company and we had shared many a story, propped up against the bar of the luxurious river steamer. It was the second day of the 1,500-kilometre voyage from Asunción to Buenos Aires, by way of the Rio Paraguay and the Rio Parana, a journey that took about three days. The return voyage against the current would take about four days.

The Padre spoke. 'When I told you I was on a drinking holiday, you didn't believe me, did you?'

I smiled and said, 'I believe you now. After hearing about your life at the mission I am surprised that you will go back. Are you going back?'

'I am.'

I remembered a topic Venancio was sure to know something about. 'There are the ruins of Jesuit missions in several places in Paraguay. What is their story?'

'Around 1600, the natives in parts of what are now Brazil, Paraguay, Uruguay, and Argentina were often subjected to the depredations of Brazilian slave raiders, the Bandeirantes. The colonial governments were indifferent or weak and the natives, including the Guarani, did not have the organisation or martial skills to defeat the raiders. The Jesuits decided that it was their mission to protect the Indians and convert them to Christianity and to a productive way of life. The story is long and complicated, but an effective resistance was mounted, and the Indians were gathered into reduccións, settlements. Fine buildings of brick and stone were constructed at each reducción and the natives were converted and taught useful skills. Creativity, in the wider sense, and dissent were discouraged with the whip. This was from about 1610 to 1767. The Jesuits had created a politically and economically powerful theocracy, a "Jesuit Republic", within the Portuguese and Spanish colonial empires. The Jesuits introduced lace production; they are long gone but Paraguay is famous for its lace.'

'What happened to the Jesuits and their theocracy?'

'By the mid-1700s, the Jesuits were under attack in some European countries, for reasons unrelated to the reduccións. The Spanish and Portuguese decided that the Jesuit Republic was too powerful and independent. The Jesuits were expelled from South America around 1767 and the reducción system dissolved after that. I am researching the history of the biggest of the reduccións, La Santísima Trinidad de Paraná, in south-eastern Paraguay, not far from Encarnación.'

I thought about his project and said, 'I have contacts at the Instituto Geográfico de la Nacional and the library. Perhaps I can find some material you can use?'

'That would be marvellous. I will write a summary of my progress and the sources I have located and what I need to know. If you can find anything else, excellent.'

'No promises, but I will try. How do I get the materials to you? I take it there is no post or postman where you are?'

'The captain of one of the river steamers will take mail to Fuerte Olimpo. The director of the factory there is helpful. He arranges for packages to be sent to one of the estancias. Someone from the mission usually passes there every month or so. Would you mind wrapping your parcel in oilcloth and sewing that into thick linen? That's the only way they can get to me dry and in one piece.'

'Sure, no problem.'

'I will give you details of who to contact.' He looked around and said, 'Who is for some bridge?'

Father de Morais, Max, and I were keen and looked around for a fourth. I saw a woman at the bar, someone I knew slightly. She agreed to join us. The woman was tall, and olive-skinned, with long shiny brunette hair, pulled up into a bun at the back of her head. She was well dressed, without standing out. Certainly, there was nothing overtly sexual about her appearance. I mention this because of her trade.

Her name was Julia Mallon, and she was a prostitute and gambler. On the first evening of the voyage, I had noticed her sitting in the bar smoking cheroots and reading a book, Joseph Conrad's novella *Heart of Darkness*, in English. I mentioned that I was reading one of Conrad's novels in Spanish and the reason why. Both of us were brushing up on our foreign languages. When I asked what she did for a living, she was quite open about her trade. She worked the steamers between Asunción and Buenos Aires, sometimes the ones on the Montevideo to Buenos Aires run.

She did the round-trip Asunción to Buenos Aires twice a month. She always booked the best cabin and was available by the night or by the voyage. No quickies, and her fees put her out of reach to any man who was not a prosperous merchant or professional. Payment in advance and only in British pounds, American dollars, or gold — usually gold Napoleons or guineas. She had some regulars, who usually engaged her for the voyage. When trade was slow, she played bridge or poker and, more often than not, she made a profit from the cards. I asked her if she ever felt in danger.

'When I was starting out, in Montevideo, I had some close calls.' She turned the left side of her neck to the light and leant her head to the right. 'Look.'

I could see a faint white scar running from low down on the left side of her throat and up the underside of her chin.

'A client did that. For no reason that I could understand. I was too quick for him, and he only grazed me. Live and learn. Ever since then I have carried this.' She opened her purse, took out a small pistol. 'This is a .25-calibre ACP Baby Browning automatic pistol.'

She removed the magazine, returned it to the grip, checked there was no round in the chamber, thumbed the safety on, and returned it to her purse. It was no toy to her. No one who saw her handle it could doubt that she knew how to use it.

'Now I make sure that everyone knows I carry the pistol, so no one gives me any trouble. Some men find it a little erotic.'

I just smiled and did not admit that the pistol did have a mildly erotic effect on me, as did her habit of smoking cigars. A sensation I tried to put aside. Sophia was enough woman for me, and I was experienced enough to know that two women at the same time were at least one too many. I explained that to Julia.

She said, 'You don't judge?'

'No. An acquaintance of mine, a prostitute, once told me that we all sell parts of ourselves, it is just a question of which part.'

Julia smiled and said, 'Just so.'

And so, an unemployed barrister, a priest, a courtesan, and a merchant of death sat down for an evening playing bridge.

Julia played conservatively and smoked as she played. Sigmund Freud may have said, 'Sometimes a cigar is only a cigar,' but I unsuccessfully tried to put aside the idea that her cigars were not 'only cigars'.

My companions gathered late each afternoon, sometimes for conversation, sometimes for cards. When Julia was free in the evening, we discussed Joseph Conrad in English and Spanish and decided that

Nostromo, set in the fictional South American Republic of Costaguana, might be literature, but it showed Conrad's limited experience of Latin America. We swapped idioms and nuances, she in Spanish, I in New Zealand English. Some of mine reduced her to baffled giggles.

Julia tried to provide equally impenetrable idioms, but what I most enjoyed was her explanations of the subtle differences of language and manners between Paraguay and Argentina and, to a lesser extent, those I would encounter in Uruguay. One night I asked her some questions that I had been dying to ask, 'What is the Latin American attitude to women in your trade?'

'Varies. For example, peasants who accept a few pesos for a quickie standing against a wall are despised by some, not by others. It is more complicated for women like me. I am well educated, well dressed, command a high price. You might say that I display a certain degree of sophistication and can hold myself out as a courtesan. I am not a street whore.'

'What do the women think about women in your trade?'

She thought about it for a second, then said, 'Some wives accept that their husband's trysts are part of an informal marriage contract. Some wives don't particularly like sex. For children yes, not for pleasure. I know some of the wives.'

'Do you ever enjoy sex with your clients?'

'You mean, do I ever have an orgasm?'

'Yes.'

'Never. But it can be pleasant. I make them shower and brush their teeth beforehand. There are rules, they obey them. When I am struggling to get through it, I just think of the alternative. Say, life in a one-horse village, married to an unpleasant man and living in grinding poverty. That does it.'

'You must earn more than you need to live?'

'I do. Some of it goes on my wardrobe. And I own property. A stylish apartment in a good part of Buenos Aires. I sometimes meet my clients there. The ones I trust, am almost friends with. This creates the illusion of exclusivity, that I am their mistress. And I own two apartments in Montevideo and one in Asunción. I have bought the entire top floor of an office building in a quiet street in Montevideo and am turning it into a loft apartment. That will be my island home, no client will ever see it.'

'You are planning your retirement?'

'I am. One day I will look in the mirror and know that I am going to have to reduce my price. That is the moment I will quit.'

'And retirement?'

'I write. I will work on that. If a good man comes along, I will marry him. I will tell him exactly how I have lived my life. Some whores make good wives, I think I will be one of them.'

She changed direction and said, 'You asked about danger and pleasure, and I told you how I cope.'

'Yes.'

'Sometimes it is a challenge not to laugh, the things some men find arousing and satisfying. I have clear limits. Acts I am not prepared to participate in. Some don't want physical contact, but just want me to say certain things, some just want me to watch. Now that is easy money. And I am discreet.'

James and Connor Travis recently returned from a flight that is believed to be the longest made in the Dominion. They flew from Dunedin to Alexandria, Queenstown, and Wanaka, traversed the Southern Alps, flew up the West Coast to Hokitika, Greymouth, and Westport and on to Farewell Spit, the northern-most point of the South Island. They returned to Dunedin by way of Nelson, Blenheim, Christchurch, Timaru, and Oamaru. They gave joyrides at each stop to raise money for the Returned Soldiers Benevolent Fund. Major

Travis, late of the staff of the New Zealand Division on the Western Front, was taught to fly by Lieutenant-Colonel Robert Smith-Barry, at the Royal Flying Corps School of Special Flying at Gosport, in 1917. The Major purchased an Avro 504K (a 2-seat biplane, usually used for training) and taught his son Connor to fly. The aeroplane was then converted to carry two passengers in the front cockpit. Part of the preparation was for petrol, oil, and spare parts to be conveyed to some of the destinations by rail and steamer.

– *Evening Star*, Dunedin. 7 January 1924

* *

One day Julia joined me for lunch. She said, 'Max tells me you are a pilot?'

'I am.'

'I thought you were a lawyer?'

'I am. And a pilot.'

'Is flying wonderful?'

'It can be.'

'Tell me about a wonderful flight.'

'My father is a pilot. When he came back from the war, he bought a surplus trainer, taught me to fly. One summer we were barnstorming and camped on the shores of Lake Wanaka next to the Wanaka Pub. Mount Aspiring is on the west side of the lake and beyond that are the fjords and the West Coast. We had been grounded by bad weather for a few days and got to know one of the sheep-station owners and his farm manager. They were keen to have a flight.

'I woke up well before dawn to find the sky clear and not a breath of wind. We decided to wake our passengers and suggest that we take them for a flight to the mountain and over to Milford Sound, a fjord and very beautiful. They were keen. Dad and I tossed up for who was to fly, and I won. It was still dark, and we had no lighting for take-off, but there was a full moon well above the horizon and the stars were bright in a clear sky. Soon we were airborne and headed for the mountain as we climbed across the lake, still and shiny in the moonlight.

'We were at fifteen hundred metres and about halfway to the mountain when the sun slowly rose. The ice and snow reflected the sunlight. It was breathtakingly beautiful as we flew across the icefields surrounding the lower parts of the mountain. From three thousand metres, we could see the West Coast and the Tasman Sea. The Southern Alps run parallel to the West Coast, and they were bathed in the sunlight. We could see Mount Cook, the highest mountain in New Zealand.

'The engine ran smoothly. The still air and the lack of vibration created the illusion that we were suspended in space. Milford Sound and the other fjords were full of cloud, shining in the sun. I flew over the owner's sheep station, and he took pictures. The station was on the western shore of the lake, and we could see his homestead, the shearing shed and other outbuildings, and a small dock with the station's barge moored to it.

'I decided to shut off the engine and glide across the lake back to our field. Those old rotary engines were unreliable, so I had plenty of practise in forced landings without power. All landings were made off a glide approach. And, if I changed my mind and had the altitude, a steep dive and an abrupt pull up would turn the engine over, so restarting would be simple.

'There was no wind at three thousand metres and no sign of surface wind. I estimated that we could glide across the lake and arrive overhead the field with at least eight hundred metres to spare. I pulled the air and petrol levers fully back. The engine noise died off and the revs dropped, the propellor became visible and flicked to a stop. I switched off and we glided in a silence broken only by the slipstream. The passengers turned around and looked a little worried. I smiled and gave them a thumbs up.

We could easily have chatted, but we decided not to break the mood. Soon we were across the lake with a thousand metres remaining. We glided over the field, I set up an approach to land, sideslipped across the fence, rounded out and touched down only ten or so metres from it. We rumbled over the rough surface and came to a halt no more than halfway across.

'Dad strolled over to us and said, "Bit cheeky, don't you think?"'

'My two passengers climbed out with huge grins on their faces. The owner pulled a wad of cash out of his pocket. He counted out 10 five-pound notes, thrust them into my hand and said, "Worth every penny." It was still only about seven in the morning, but we adjourned to the pub, woke up the publican and the station owner insisted on shouting.'

Julia looked puzzled and said, 'Shouting?'

'Paying for someone's drinks, that day he shouted everyone.'

'That flight sounds wonderful. I want you to take me flying.'

'It was special, in the mountains, above the glaciers, the air crystal clear and smooth, no wind. Often the air is rough and visibility limited. And I don't have an aeroplane.'

'Argentina has mountains and glaciers. Some days are clear and windless.'

I promised nothing but said I would try to arrange a flight for her. She said, 'How do you find Paraguay and the Paraguayans?'

'They have been welcoming and friendly. At least most of them, most of the time.'

I did not mention my encounter with Bray. I thought of an anecdote, about Ángel Garcia.

'Sometimes they surprise me. I went to a colleague's place for dinner. A small house but freshly painted and scrupulously clean. Next door was a field with half a dozen cows. One of them broke through a rickety fence and started grazing in the back garden. My colleague went out to check. He came back, took his pistol from its holster and went back outside. A few minutes passed and we heard two shots. He came back in, and I asked what had happened. The cow had broken in twice before. He had warned the owner that if it happened again, he — my colleague — would shoot the cow. It had happened again, so he led the cow back into the field and shot it dead. I asked him if he would get into trouble. He looked surprised and told me that the Army would not let that happen. This is one more piece of evidence suggesting that the Army is a political force, and its members have privileges that most civilians do not.'

The voyage was a wonderful holiday, and the people were interesting, even Max. But all too soon we arrived. On the third morning, the steamer docked in Buenos Aires. I was about to walk down the gangplank when Julia walked up and gave me a slip of paper and said, 'Stay in touch, this is how to contact me.'

I tipped my hat and bowed a little. I was halfway down the gangplank when she added, 'And just remember, Buenos Aires is the most stylish city in Europe.'

* *

Within a few hours, I found this Delphic utterance to be true. I arrived at the hotel, a very grand one, checked in and was shown what I had been expecting, what must have been the smallest and cheapest room. There was a lift, it clanked and swayed, often breaking down.

Later that morning I found an elegant pavement café, one that would not have been out of place in Paris and started to refine my plan. I had met with San Martin the day before departure, and he gave me details of the type of aircraft that I should look for. There was one I should definitely inspect, and perhaps I would hear about some others. I returned to the hotel and made a telephone call, setting up a meeting for the next day. I checked prices at the hotel restaurant, confirmed my guess that they were eyewatering, went out and found an affordable meal. The voyage and been fun but very social, and I looked forward to resting and turned in early. The room had a large, comfortable bed and the murmur of traffic far below was conducive to restful, restorative sleep.

The next morning I rented a car, an old Austin 7 with a body of wood and fabric. I drove out to the airfield at Mendoza in search of my contact. Everyone knew everyone else at the airfield and I soon found the man and the aeroplane I was looking for. It was outside a hangar and the owner was polishing the windscreens when I walked up. I introduced myself, we talked and agreed that I would inspect the logbooks, do a walk-around inspection, and then fly it. My research had turned up material on the type.

The Junkers A50 Junior is not only an excellent sport and school plane for beginners and advanced pupils but also a superior plane for the former airplane pilot, who wishes to keep in practice and prefers an easily flown, airplane … For a light two-seater which must be absolutely reliable and capable of carrying two persons with baggage at high speed a distance of 600 km (373 miles) and have a high ceiling and a low landing speed, it was necessary to have an engine possessing a great reserve power, reliability and endurance. The Junkers Junior is equipped with the air-cooled five-cylinder Armstrong Siddeley Genet engine … The Junkers Junior can be used in summer or winter, on land or on water, in the tropics or in the far north. It is an adaptable non-sensitive light airplane of high performance …

– National Advisory Committee for Aeronautics. *Aircraft Circular No. 118: The Junkers Junior Light Airplane (German)*. 1930

The Junkers A50 Junior was a neat-looking, two-seat open cockpit trainer and sports aeroplane. Its construction was the same as the F 13, a low wing monoplane with a cantilever wing, all-metal, and skinned with the corrugated Duralumin sheets used in all contemporary Junkers aircraft. I examined the airframe and engine logbooks and saw that they were up to date, and that the aeroplane and its motor had done less than 350 hours. It was well maintained, with no obvious defects. I said to the owner, 'Can you give me some dual instruction on it?'

He said, 'I am not a pilot. We should go to the airfield café and see who is available.'

We found an instructor with time on his hands, a German named Fritz Sauber, a tall, thin man of about thirty-five with blond hair cut short and going prematurely grey. If I had to characterise his look in one word, it would be Prussian. He had flown the Junkers and he agreed to give me sixty minutes of instruction. He asked for my logbook and licence. I showed him my 'B' licence and a notarised summary of my flying experience. A man of few words, his Spanish was spare and delivered with a strong German accent. He grunted and his look suggested that he would soon find out if I could fly.

Sauber did a meticulous preflight inspection. Soon we were in the air and could see much of the city and some of the River Plate Estuary. We had agreed on a flight plan. I did some steep turns, explored the low-speed handling, stalled and recovered a couple of times, then prepared to spin the aeroplane. The entry was smooth, and the recovery was immediate. I did a spin the other way and Sauber signalled that I should try a loop. The engine was only eighty-five horsepower, so I had to use full power and dive to attain the entry speed. The loop was straightforward, and I was impressed by the handling and performance. Sauber signalled that he had control and did a perfect barrel roll to the right, recovered, and barrel-rolled smoothly to the left. I took over and he pointed to the airfield. I flew overhead and descended to circuit height. We were third behind two Air Force trainers doing circuits and bumps. I did a touch and go, took off, did another touch a go and then a full stop, landing and taxied in. I was impressed, this was the type of aeroplane we needed, modern, easy to fly, economical, and with a structure that was resistant to the elements. I was also impressed with Sauber; his airmanship and handling were excellent.

I followed the advice I had got from a car dealer on how to negotiate a purchase: acknowledge the good points but do not be too enthusiastic. The owner named his price and said that he would require a bank draft or cash in US dollars or British pounds. I told him I was impressed with his aeroplane but would have to report and ask for instructions and that I would phone him as soon as I had. I found Sauber, who had thawed a bit, and was evidently satisfied that I could fly. He would not accept money but said I could buy him a drink. I asked him to recommend an evening bar. By one of those fortunate coincidences, it was the café I had been intending to visit. Perhaps there would be a Bolivian or two there. Sauber would be a perfect cover. We agreed to meet that evening at seven.

I sat in the airfield café watching the flying. In addition to the Air Force, there were private owners, an aeroclub and a gliding club. A charter outfit operated from a hangar with a small office tacked onto it. A large, shiny car pulled up outside the office and a well-dressed man and woman got out and were ushered into a Waco biplane with an enclosed cabin for a pilot, three passengers, and luggage. The chauffeur transferred luggage from the boot of the car into the aeroplane and a uniformed pilot climbed aboard. The Waco started, taxied out and took off, circling overhead before heading off to the north-east.

The gliding club was operating. A winch mounted on a small truck was in place on the boundary of the aerodrome and its wire was laid out parallel to the runway. The glider was a primary, the most basic aircraft imaginable, an open frame with a single seat at the front (the pilot totally exposed), a wing above the frame, and a tail unit. The pilot, probably a pupil (solo, no instructor), was being taught the basics by being dragged along by the winch, fast enough to make the controls effective but too slow for him to become airborne. The glider yawed left and right, the left wing dropped and dragged along the ground raising a plume of dust. The glider came to a stop and a stripped-down Ford Model T drove out and towed the wire and glider back to the start point, an instructor holding the wing level and deep in conversation with the pupil.

I spent the rest of the day watching the flying. So far, my mission had been a paid holiday; soon things might get serious. I drove back to the hotel and got ready for my evening out. One of my jobs was to seek out technical books, a job I was looking forward to. Being paid to fly, spend time in bookshops and explore a beautiful city. A dream. For now.

The café was a twenty-minute walk from the hotel, through streets lined with handsome buildings.

The German was waiting, and his drink of choice was a shot glass of peach schnapps and a large glass of pale lager beer. He took the full glass of schnapps and dropped it into the beer glass. He turned to me and said, 'We call it a depth charge. You should try one.'

I did. You drank the beer, retrieved the shot glass, and drank the remains of its contents in one gulp. We ordered another round. And a third. Within half an hour of my arrival, I was suffused with a mellow glow and decided to pace myself. The German said, 'How did you like the Junior?'

'I like it. I hope we buy it.'

'Who is we?'

'Paraguay.'

'How did you come to be in Paraguay? You are English, aren't you?'

I gave in to my tendency to be precise and said, 'From New Zealand, formerly a British colony, now a self-governing Dominion in the British Empire.'

He grunted and looked a question. I continued and told him about my pierhead jump and the voyage to Asunción. I said, 'Paraguay is a little strange, but it is growing on me.'

Sauber had a lewd expression on his face. 'You mean you have found a woman.'

I had not thought of my decision to stay in quite that way, but it was true, at least in part. I said, 'There was nothing for me at home, there is in Paraguay. And yes, I have found a woman. And there is competition for her time and affections.'

This time he made a face that I can only describe as salacious. I was not going to be drawn on the subject of Sophia. He thought for a moment and said something so idiomatic, I did not catch its meaning. I asked for clarification. It was: 'She works on the principle of treat them mean, keep them keen.'

I laughed out loud, and so did he. He was establishing himself as good company, as well as a first-class aviator. He said, 'I read something about a long, soaring flight by a sailplane in Paraguay. Do you know anything about that?'

'I was the pilot.'

This immediately opened a new topic of conversation, and for half an hour, our talk was peppered with terms such as glide angle, minimum sinking speed, adverse yaw, and the like. Impenetrable to a listener, but rich in meaning for a pilot. His many questions and observations of a technical nature revealed an impressive depth and breadth of knowledge of aviation. After we had exhausted the topic, I asked him, 'How do you come to be in Argentina?'

'The Polish stole my land, and everything on it. After the Great War. My family has owned estates in East Prussia for hundreds of years, perhaps since the days of the Teutonic Knights. Germany lost the war; President Wilson reneged on his promise that the peace would be fair and equitable; Poland was created, and our land was stolen from us and given to them.'

He was another one of those dispossessed Germans who were found all over South America in those days. He went on, 'I fought them, the Poles, with the Freikorps in Silesia.'

The depth charges were having their effect and he went off on a tangent. 'I was a pilot in the Imperial Air Service. I ended the war flying R-planes.'

He was talking about the giant German bombers, some of them with wingspans of forty metres or more, and up to six engines. This started another long technical discussion. This time it was me asking the questions and hanging on his every word. By this time, he was on his fifth or sixth depth charge, but I had shifted to espressos and beer. Eventually, we got back to the subject of his personal history. He had been cheerful when we talked flying, but now he became morose.

'After Silesia, I looked for a place to settle. The Latvians were offering land to anyone who fought for them against the Reds in their Independence War. I joined Sachsenberg and flew Junkers D1s and J2s.'

I said, 'I met a man called Kurt Buckler at a party; I think he was in the same unit.'

Sauber said, 'He was a good man, a good pilot.'

I asked, 'What happened in Latvia?'

'We defeated the Reds, then the Allies ordered all German units to withdraw from the Baltic States. The Latvians thought they no longer needed us and told us to leave. We mounted a successful coup in Riga, and the situation became even more chaotic. The various factions and armies were fighting each other. Many died, some of them my friends. Eventually, we had to return to Germany, where I had no home, no job, no prospects. So I went to the office of a steamship line and used money loaned to me by an old comrade to buy a third-class ticket to Buenos Aires. I have been here ever since. You know, don't you, that Germany would have won the Great War had we not been stabbed in the back by the socialists and intellectuals? And that the post-war treaties left seventeen million Germans living outside of Germany or Austria?'

Buckler had said the same thing, word for word. That was the first time that I had heard this theory, the stab-in-the-back, which was being peddled by the extreme right in Germany, and when coupled with a revanchist desire to gather all Germans together in a Greater Germany, would cause carnage only a few years later.

'What are you doing in Argentina? I mean, what do you do, apart from flying?' I asked.

'I work as a consultant for a company setting up an airline. Reasonably well paid, and I will be chief pilot when and if it gets off the ground, no pun intended. At the moment their fleet consists of two Waco planes. I fly them on charters and surveys. The plan is that operating these aircraft will help us to establish ourselves and that in due course we will buy and operate airliners on scheduled services. This depression makes it difficult to obtain financing for anything as speculative as an airline. And Argentina has a well-developed railway network. That is what we will be competing against. There is no way of predicting whether we will attract enough traffic to make it viable. And money will have to change hands before we get our operators' certificate.'

'I saw one of your aeroplanes depart with a prosperous couple aboard.'

'Was the woman attractive and much younger than the man?'

'She was.'

'Probably a banker or a lawyer and his mistress off to Punta del Este, in south-east Uruguay.'

He used an unfamiliar expression. He explained its meaning. The closest equivalent in English would be 'they flew off for a dirty weekend'.

Two well-dressed men in suits and ties arrived and one of them greeted Fritz with one word: 'Poker?'

He said yes and looked at me. 'Do you play?'

I told him that I did, and he introduced me. The men were diplomats, a Uruguayan and a Peruvian, and soon we were deep in a game. It became clear that Sauber and his friends were serious, skilled players. The Peruvian offered cigars, the strong black ones that General Belaieff favoured.

I played conservatively and by the time the game broke up, I was about even. I said my goodbyes and walked back to my hotel.

* *

As I was about to step into the lift at the hotel, Julia walked out.

'How about a nightcap?' she said.

I was pleased to see her and immediately agreed. We settled on stools at the bar and ordered drinks. I said, 'Have you been working?'

'Yes. A regular.'

'Tell me about some of your clients. I am sure that it is good practice to keep their identities secret. But with no names or details that would identify them, there is no problem. As my father would say, "No names, no pack drill."' Julia raised an eyebrow.

I explained, 'In the army, pack drill is a punishment for infractions of the regulations. Running around and around in a circle with an NCO shouting at the soldier. Sweaty and most unpleasant. But if a soldier is naughty, and his identity is not known, he can't be punished; that is, he does not have to do the pack drill. Tell you what, I will swap you, one of my anecdotes for one of yours. Toss you for who goes first?'

'Yes.'

I took a coin, flipped it into the air and slammed it down on the bar with my hand covering it. She called heads.

We looked. 'Tails, you're first.'

'Sometimes I do not even have to touch my client,' Julia began. 'There is a man, quite a nice one. He presented me with a black cloche hat, black riding boots, and a leather riding crop. We meet in his office, which has a loose carpet on the floor. He undresses and sits on a chair watching me. He tells me to undress. This is all a detailed ritual. I undress and put on the hat and boots and hold the whip. Then I take over and make him lay down. I roll him up into the carpet until he is trapped in it, with only his head showing. I walk around slapping my riding crop against my boots. Then I sit in a chair facing him and talk to him in a low voice. I am firm but not abusive. That is all. I unroll him, I get dressed, he gets dressed, I leave.'

'How can you do this without laughing?'

'It is just business. And it is infinitely preferable to full sex when all I want to do is go home, soak in a bath and read detective novels. It is easy money. Your turn.'

I laughed. 'My mind is blank. You distracted me.' I thought for a while and then said, 'I know.' I described a criminal client of mine who had been arrested during a burglary. He was exceptionally difficult to deal with and I had to withdraw. He tried to block payment of my fee, instructed another lawyer, was convicted, tried to appeal on the grounds that his new lawyer was incompetent, lost and served a term of imprisonment. This was the third time he had been sent to prison. Since then, he has been arrested twice, convicted twice, and been sent to prison twice.

'The point of my story is that some men are deluded about how clever they are and continue to believe this in the face of all the evidence to the contrary.'

Julia smiled. 'Tell me some more lawyer stories.'

I thought for a moment and said, 'These are two anecdotes about other lawyers. There is a story told about a KC, a King's Counsel, a senior and capable advocate. He had defended a woman on a serious charge and had arrived home, exhausted from two weeks in the service of a client who insisted on putting forward a defence that could not succeed. The phone rang, the KC listened briefly, said, "Seven years," and hung up. When asked who had rung, he said, "The accused's husband, asking when she would be home to cook dinner.'"

Julia laughed.

I said, 'Another lawyer, a solicitor specialising in commercial law, had a difficult client ring up early one Sunday morning, demanding instant advice and action. The solicitor, suffering from a hangover, listened for a time, and then said, "How much would I have to pay you for you to take your problems to another lawyer, do not talk, just tell me how much?" After a brief silence, the client said, "Fifty pounds." The lawyer said, "Your file and a cheque for fifty pounds will be at reception for you first thing on Monday morning." And hung up.'

Julia said, 'And you have devoted part of your life to representing these people?'

I agreed that I had and might do so in the future. We talked about the ethics of clients who were obviously guilty. I went on to give my standard explanation of why we must deliver justice for all, also that an advocate's job was to defend, not to judge. I reminded Julia that all of us sell part of ourselves and it is just a question of which part.

Julia said, 'What part have you sold?'

I had thought about that since my first visit to Café Eiffel. 'Some of my moral certainty, some of my confidence that I would never be hated or be in danger from another human being. Clients, even when their lawyers are managing the client's affairs honestly and competently, can be very threatening. A Chinese client brought his bodyguard, a squat, tattooed enforcer to a meeting where his only purpose was to make me take the client seriously. The client left town suddenly, and although he had no reason to doubt that I was being diligent, I got a visit at home, on a Sunday, from a large man with many rough tattoos, including boob marks — dots tattooed below the left eye. One dot for each year served in prison. He had a dog with him, the kind they use in the fighting pits. He did not introduce himself but talked about his dog. He took it off the chain and said that it was trained to kill, but only if he told it to. He put it back on the chain and left the property. I did not think that the client would harm me, but it certainly damaged my peace of mind.'

Julia told me that she was wilting and had to go home. She kissed me on both cheeks, we agreed to meet again in a few days, and she was gone.

Before I went to bed, I coded up my report about the Junkers Junior and first thing the next morning, took it to the telegraph office.

* *

For the next few days, I worked my way through the list of bookshops in the phone book, without finding anything worth buying but having a pleasant and undemanding time of it. I spent time in cafés watching the world go by. I salvaged something of this part of my mission by compiling a list of aviation journals that I needed for my task of checking published material for anything about Bolivian air capabilities. I had a sudden thought. Major manufacturers of aircraft often published in-house journals and local newspapers would publish detailed and frequent reports on their activities. I resolved to identify companies that might supply aircraft to Bolivia and to get on their mailing lists, and to subscribe to the local papers.

I was still trailing my coat, with no real expectation that I would be approached. Spending time playing poker with my new German friend meant that a widening circle of acquaintances knew where I was from and what I was doing. Sending coded telegrams increased the chances that I would be noticed and recognised as a person of interest to Bolivia.

One evening Fritz introduced me to his boss. We finished cards early, and I stayed for a drink and chatted to the manager about his project. He was not an aviator, but he was well informed and appeared to be interested in what I had to say. He offered to pay for my time, as a sort of consultant. I was happy to talk aviation for nothing, and we agreed that he would buy the drinks, and, if he needed further advice, we would settle on a fee. I was puzzled because Fritz could have answered any of the questions the man put to me, and he, the manager, seemed to have a first-class understanding of the technicalities. I thought that perhaps he wanted a second opinion. Anyway, I needed no encouragement to hold forth on my favourite topic.

A few days after sending my message about the aeroplane, I received a reply. It authorised the purchase for the asking price and instructed me to collect a banker's draft, to close the purchase, and to fly the Junior back to Ñu Guasú. I rang the owner and we settled on a time for us to meet, then took delivery of the draft, and drove out to the airfield. I was about to inspect the aeroplane one more time when the owner said, 'Hold off for half an hour. I need to have the magnetos reinstalled.'

'Is there a problem with them?'

'No, it is just that buyers have been known to take delivery of an aeroplane and depart without the formality of paying.'

'And you suspected me?'

'No, but Paraguay is an awful long way from here.'

Half an hour later the magnetos were back in place. The engine operated perfectly when I ran it up. I handed over the cheque and received the logbooks and a signed bill of sale. The weather was not good, and I was in no hurry to leave and wanted one more night in town. I talked to the manager of Fritz's company, and he said I could leave my new purchase in his hangar overnight. We chatted and he told me that he was having trouble finding aircraft that were suitable for his airline. He explained his requirements and hinted that a finder's fee would be payable if I could find one for him. I told him that I was unlikely to find one as there were no airlines, or even charter companies, where I was going.

I had arranged to meet Julia for a drink in the hotel bar. She held her drink well but that night she was more than a little drunk and upset and a bit garrulous. Eventually, she told me what was upsetting her. She had a long-term client who was a married man, terrified that his wife would find out about his liaison. Instead of ending it with her, he demanded that she give up her life of prostitution and become his mistress. She had refused point-blank. He had not taken it well when reminded that the relationship with her was, and always had been, a commercial transaction. He had become threatening and only stopped when she had reached into her handbag for the pistol. She had looked at him and conveyed non-verbally that if he did not leave, things would get sticky.

She was so upset, she said, something that surprised me. Always discreet, she had never told me the name or occupation of any of her clients. She was drunk and angry and this time she named him, along with some very nasty characterisations. I recognised the name instantly. Her jealous, violent client was the Bolivian Military Attaché.

I said, 'What are you going to do?'

'Take a few weeks off. Maybe go home to Montevideo.'

'Do you still want me to take you flying?'

'Absolutely.'

'I have an aeroplane I am flying to Asunción, and if the weather is good, I am off at first light tomorrow. Do you want to come?'

She smiled for the first time that night. 'Yes, I do.'

'Meet me here at six in the morning. The hotel has arranged transport. There's only room for you and a toothbrush. So, travel light. One small bag is acceptable.'

It was still dark when the manager and I rolled the hangar doors open and pushed the aircraft out onto the tarmac. The weather was perfect, a light wind from the west and no cloud. I topped up the fuel tank and did a preflight inspection. Julia, stylish as always, was wearing a heavy leather coat, a colourful scarf, whipcord jodhpurs, and expensive-looking ankle boots. I handed her a leather helmet, goggles, and leather gauntlets. I was helping her settle into the open cockpit when I had a thought, and said, 'You smiled at the manager. Do you know him? A client perhaps?'

'Not a client. He spends a lot of time with the Bolivian. The attaché.'

Chapter Ten
A Coup d'État. 24 April 1932

Estigarribia looked at me across the table. 'My first instinct was to trust you, and that instinct was clearly the correct one.'

On the table between us were stacked gold coins that we conservatively estimated to be worth twenty-five thousand US dollars. More, much more, remained close to where I had found it, about half a million dollars in total. In 1932, that was enough to buy a fine house with servants, a holiday house somewhere expensive, cars, a private plane, and investments a man could live off and live well for the rest of his life.

'You could have taken the money and slipped out of the country.'

'I thought about it. But Paraguay has been good to me, I have a job doing what I love, a house, friends. A life with meaning.'

'And you are in love?'

I was not sure about that. 'Perhaps.'

I did not say that I was not so sure I would have got away. Powerful people knew the location of the gold. They had not been able to retrieve it, but they had eyes all over Paraguay. By now they knew that I had salvaged the plane and they would be monitoring my movements. I could have simply flown away in the Junkers. To anywhere within about fifteen hundred kilometres. But where could I go in an aeroplane with no identity or paperwork and no plausible excuse for my arrival in it? It would be impounded and thoroughly searched. At best I would lose the gold and keep my freedom, having lost all I had in Paraguay. The other options were not attractive. There was no airline service from Paraguay to the outside world. I would have to either use the river or the railways to move myself and the gold. If I were seen to be leaving the country, they would have plenty of time to track me down. And when they did, I would be silenced. They would want to know what I knew and who I had told. To be sure I had told them everything, my death would be slow and painful. They would kill me twice, once to make me talk, and once to stop me talking.

There was no going back, I had found the gold and contacted Estigarribia. I had also found a document case and a map case. Lists of code names and addresses, street maps, and diagrams of buildings were spread out on another table. Estigarribia had spent a silent hour examining them and making notes.

As soon as Julia told me the Attaché had a connection with the manager of the airline, I knew I had missed something in the F 13. A friend of the Bolivian Military Attaché had offered me a fee to find an aeroplane. More precisely, had asked me to locate an aeroplane that could carry the pilot and four or five passengers or five hundred kilograms of cargo. The only aeroplane in Paraguay that matched that description was the mystery Junkers we had salvaged from the Chaco and that now sat, covered in dust sheets, in the back of a hangar at the airbase. He did not want a plane or the plane, he wanted something hidden in it.

The flight from Buenos Aires had been pleasant. Clear skies, a magnificent view of unfamiliar terrain. And yet I was distracted by what I had just learned. We refuelled once and landed at Ñu Guasú in the early evening as the sun was going down. I drove Julia into the city and dropped her at her apartment. She gave me her telephone number and agreed to meet for a drink sometime soon.

I wanted to search the F 13 as soon as possible, but I could not do it during the day. I would have to wait until only the night guards were at the airfield. I often worked in the evening, so there would be nothing suspicious about what I was planning to do. It helped that my duties were varied and required me to visit almost every part of the base from time to time. I timed my arrival at the airfield so it was half an hour after everyone except the guard detail had gone home. I was waved past the guardhouse. I parked behind the hangars, walked to the administration building and opened my office. I sat down and thought things through. If I was going to act, I had to do it now. And I had to search the aeroplane without arousing any undue attention. The F 13 had been sitting forgotten because the staff had greater priorities, and I had promised to go over it and prepare a list of jobs that needed to be done. I found a clipboard, paper and pencil, and a torch and walked to the hangar.

I turned on the lights and locked the door. The guard toured the base roughly every two hours and had been returning to the guardhouse when I parked, so it was unlikely I would be disturbed. I selected some tools from a workbench and pulled the dust cover back so I could enter by the cabin door on the left side of the fuselage. Once inside, I pulled the dust sheet down and shut the door.

The most likely place to hide contraband was under the sheets of plywood screwed to the floor of the cabin. If it were heavy, it would be as close to the centre of gravity as possible, and that was immediately behind the pilot's seat, so I started there. The long-range tank in the front of the cabin had been removed a few weeks before. I found the correct size screwdriver and went to work on the plywood sheet that covered the floor across the width of the fuselage. I removed the screws and levered the sheet up. Underneath it were twenty canvas bags, each with a leather handle sewn into the top. On top of them was a leather document case and a large canvas map case. I opened the document case and found typed lists and diagrams. The map case contained maps and charts. The bags contained gold coins. I took a handful of coins and let them run through my figures back into the bag.

It was no mystery why the arms had been stacked in plain sight while the gold and documents were hidden under the floorboards. If the pilot had known they were there, he would have been perfectly placed to disappear with the aeroplane, the arms, and the gold. If he had an entrepreneurial turn of mind, he could have found a buyer for the maps and other documents.

Was that all? I unscrewed the other floorboards and found nothing. I replaced the boards and screwed them down over the empty spaces. I sat and thought it through. I had already inspected the rest of the aeroplane with a torch and mirror, had looked into every space and seen nothing. I had found all that there was to be found.

I needed time and a place to think. I replaced the document case, map case and bags, screwed the sheet of wood down, and left the aeroplane with the door closed and the dust sheet back where it had been. I turned the lights off, locked the hangar door, and returned to my office. In my desk draw was a compact 9 mm Browning automatic pistol. I checked the magazine and replaced it, pulled the slide back to chamber a round, put the safety on, and put it in my pocket. In another desk drawer, there was a bottle of whisky and two glasses. I put the bottle and a glass on the desk and then changed my mind and returned them to the drawer.

I went for a walk along the boundaries of the airfield and found myself near the guardhouse. The Sergeant of the Guard was a coffee drinker, unlike most Paraguayans, and I sometimes shared coffee with him and chatted. I contributed a kilogram of coffee from time to time. He invited me in, and he talked about his garden. My knowledge of the subject was nil, but his enthusiasm was infectious, and I found about his favourite flowers, shrubs and trees. It was curiously soothing to hear about such a benign topic at such a highly charged moment.

My choices were simple. Do nothing, after all, this was not my country. Or do something. I decided to do something. I finished my coffee, thanked the Sergeant, and departed with a smile and a cross between a wave and a salute.

I had decided to take one of the bags of gold plus the maps and documents and find someone trustworthy to confide in. If I tried to transfer all the gold to the car, I would probably be noticed. Even if I loaded it without being seen, the suspension would sag and be noticed. But I couldn't leave it in the plane. While I was thinking, I noticed the crates of books sitting in the corner and had an idea. The plan required a window of time where I would not be bothered by the guards.

I found a chair and opened the small door set into the sliding doors at the front of the hangar. I sat down and lit a cigar. I sat there smoking until the guard came by after their inspection and were on the way back to the guardhouse. I offered cigars, which were accepted. While we smoked them down, we chatted about the local football teams. The Sergeant and one of the Privates supported different teams and engaged in a spirited argument about the merits of their favourite players. I have no interest in team sports and can't understand why who wins or loses should be of such interest to grown men, but I have learned not to say so. The talk turned to a bullfight both men had seen the past weekend in San Lorenzo. The technicalities were way over my head. Finally, the cigars were finished, and the men strolled away.

I looked at my watch. I had about two hours but decided that for safety's sake, I must be finished in under an hour and thirty minutes. I went back into the hangar, locked the front door, and checked that the back door was locked. The glass on the windows was frosted, and the windows were high up so a casual passer-by could not see in. I unscrewed the floorboard that concealed the gold and documents in the F 13 and put it aside. I took one of the bags and the document and map cases and set them by the back door. I opened the door and looked around and there was no one in sight. I picked up the three items and walked to my car and opened the boot. I lifted the fabric of the lining, hauled the spare wheel out, and put it on the ground. I put my packages in the recess, replaced the lining, put the wheel on top, and closed and locked the boot.

Someone shouted, 'Travis.' I felt a shot of ice water to my heart and looked around. It was one of the mechanics who had built the glider. He wasn't on duty, why was he here? He walked towards me from the direction of the guardhouse. He was a little unsteady on his feet and had a bottle in his left hand.

He walked up to me, smiling. 'A son, and a daughter!' he said. I remembered that his wife was pregnant with their first child. He added, 'I have just come from the hospital, a son and a daughter!' He reached into a pocket and pulled out two shot glasses. He said, 'They told me you were here, you must drink with me.'

He filled the glasses from the bottle and handed one to me, saying, 'To my daughter.' We emptied our glasses in one draught. It was a sugary rum. He refilled them and said, 'To my son.' We drank. He said, 'One more, for their mother'. He filled the glasses and we drank again.

He said, 'What are you doing here at this time of night, stealing the Colonel's paperclips?' He laughed at his own joke.

I said, 'Great news, but I must get back to work.'

He said, 'I will be in the guardhouse if you want another drink.'

I walked back to the hangar and locked the door behind me. I had thrown down three shots of overproof rum on an empty stomach. After a fright like that, it was exactly what I needed. The sensation was delightful. I tried to concentrate.

The crates of books were stacked three high and I dragged the top layer down and clear of the pile. Next, I levered open the four crates closest to the wall. I removed all but the bottom layer of books. I put five of the bags of gold in each of three crates and four bags in the fourth. Then I stacked books tightly around each nest of bags and packed three layers of books on top of them. Finally, I nailed the tops back on and smeared dust over the marks caused by the crowbar and over the nail holes, and I dragged the top layer of crates back into place. All of this was hard work and unaided it took a long time. There was a small disused office in the opposite corner of the hangar. I cleared out oily rags, empty petrol and oil cans, and tarpaulins and packed the surplus books under a wooden bench, covering them with the junk. An hour and forty-five minutes had passed. The guard would be coming by any minute.

I put some dirty, oily rags around the head of a broom and brushed out the fresh drag marks on the floor. Then I screwed the floorboard back down in the plane and smeared dirt and oil over the heads of the screws. I climbed out, shut the cabin door, and pulled the dust sheet back over the plane. I had a last look around and could not see anything out of place. I picked up the torch, clipboard and pencil and walked back to the office. I was exhausted.

I reviewed what I knew. The aeroplane and its contents were Bolivian. They were planning and financing some kind of operation, almost certainly on Paraguayan soil. It could not be an all-Bolivian operation as they would be detected before mounting it and, even if they did strike, they could never get away afterwards. And there was nothing of military value that they could achieve.

Bolivia was arming and financing a group of Paraguayans who would carry out some operation that would benefit Bolivia. The Paraguayan conspirators, or at least some of them, must be military. There was no way for radical change in Paraguay that would not require the co-operation of at least part of the Paraguayan Armed Forces. If Air Force officers were involved, they would have known about the arrival of my Junkers and would have moved to retrieve the cargo. So, no Air Force officer was involved. Who could I trust? I still couldn't decide.

I had seen Estigarribia several times since our talk on the riverbank at Puerto Casado. I had to trust someone, and I chose him. Something about his manner, his contentment with his house, family and his life, was reassuring.

I arrived at the house just before midnight and rang the bell. A maid answered and I asked to see the Colonel. I had just sat down on a chair in the hall when he appeared. I must have woken him, but he seemed untroubled and wide awake. I thought that perhaps he was one of those soldiers with four in the morning courage. On my last visit, I looked at the family photos on the piano. There was one dated 1916 of Estigarribia and his wife on their wedding day. He looked uncomfortable in his white dress uniform, holding a Pickelhaube, an ornate Prussian style helmet with a large spike on top. For reasons I could not quite understand, I found it reassuring that this cool and courageous warrior was human enough to be nervous on his wedding day.

He invited me into his study, and he waited for me to tell him why I needed to see him at this hour.

I put the canvas bag on his desk, opened it, and started to stack the gold in front of him. He raised an eyebrow but said nothing. Then I gave him the document case and map case. After he finished taking notes, he said, 'Tell me the whole story.'

I told him everything that had happened from the day I sailed for Buenos Aires to the moment I arrived at his house. He asked me for my opinion on what was happening and why. I told him what I thought and asked him what he thought. He nodded and said, 'The plan is for a regime change, or a change in the high command of the Army and Navy, or both. I can eliminate one possibility. The conspirators are not planning to surrender the Chaco to Bolivia. Any group who announced such a policy would be dragged out and shot by the mob. So, it has to be something else, and I think I know what it is. Did I tell you that I have made five long journeys through the Chaco?'

'No.'

'I have, and I can honestly say that I endured great hardships, but it had to be done. To defeat Bolivian aggression, we must know the terrain. Did I meet you at the General's party?'

'Yes.'

'And you know that he has conducted many expeditions through the Chaco?'

'I do.'

'Well, his cover was simple exploration and to study the Indians, but the primary reason was to compile military maps. The two of us have collaborated and have produced the most detailed maps ever made of the area. Maps for soldiers. We know more than any white man has ever known about the area. The army that knows the most about terrain, water, and areas where armies can manoeuvre, will have a decisive advantage. There are still areas we know little or nothing about.

'Which brings me to the nub of the problem. I am certain that the correct strategy is to contest the interior. Fight as far away from the Rio Paraguay as we can. The alternative is to retreat to the river and let them come to us. The high command is divided over the issue. I was appointed Chief of Staff of the Army in 1928 but was removed because my opinions on strategy were not welcome.

'The river is fifteen hundred kilometres long, and we do not have nearly enough men and armaments to protect it. If the Bolivians reach the river, they will create forts in strategic places, they will lay minefields in the river and cover them with batteries of artillery. The artillery will outrange any weapon carried by our new gunboats. The northern front, up around Fortin Vanguardia and Bahia Negra, will be cut off. The river is the only way to transport large numbers of men and the supplies of food and ammunition they need to fight. They will be starved out and Bolivia will control the northern Chaco.

'There are rivers that flow through north-eastern Bolivia and into the Paraguay. The Bolivians have a large fleet of shallow draught steamers and barges. And at least one small gunboat. They would not dare enter the upper Rio Paraguay because our new gunboats would sink them before they could get in range, but they would do it if the gunboats were blockaded into the lower Paraguay. They could also create a shipyard on the west bank, float sections of warships down to it, and assemble them. Then they could contest control of the river. We believe that their grand strategy is to cross the river, occupy Eastern Paraguay, and stay there until we concede everything they want and pay an indemnity for their war costs. The Brazilians, Argentinians, and Uruguayans did that to us after they defeated us in 1870. Brazil and Argentina annexed large areas of Paraguay and compelled us to sign a treaty recording the fait accompli.

'If Bolivia wins, there will be a Bolivian city and harbour within sight of our capital and Paraguay will be a hostage to Bolivian power for as long as she survives. She may not survive.'

There was a long silence. I added my two cents' worth. 'There are a lot of maybes and uncertainties in what you have said.'

'There are, nothing is certain in war. The belief that we should defend the west bank is not irrational. Part of the reasoning is that Bolivian supply lines will be very long and inefficient. That is true, and Bolivian soldiers will have come a great distance before they fight. We could send parties to raid some of their supply lines, but only the fifty kilometres or so closest to the river. They will not have to defend most of them. And they can build roads, even narrow-gauge railways, unmolested. They will take over our railways at Puerto Pinasco, Casado, Sastre, Guarani. There are others, including two railways on the east bank. We can destroy them as we retreat, but we can't destroy the right of way and they are on the Decauville system, with their track designed to be laid and repaired quickly. They can restore several track systems in only a few months.

'Anyway, I think that the riverbank defence strategy would be a fatal mistake. At the very least, a west bank defence strategy would greatly increase Bolivia's prospects of success. Doctor José Patricio Guggiari is President, you would have met him at the General's. He is in favour of a forward defence, as far forward as possible. The Vice-President is for a riverbank strategy, and so are many officers. I think they intend to depose the President in favour of the Vice-President.'

I said, 'Why have the plotters made no attempt to collect the gold? They must have known where it was for weeks.'

'Because they were indecisive. A failed attempt would have led to the discovery of gold and documents and the unmasking of their plan. Indecision is fatal when you aim to overthrow a government. Trust me on this point, I have experience in these matters.'

'What are you going to do?'

'Act decisively. First, though, I want you to count out a thousand of these coins. I am not a banker and don't know the gold price, but they should be worth at least five thousand US dollars, perhaps twice as much. The gold is yours.'

'Why are you giving me that much or any?'

'Like it or not, you are involved in a coup and countercoup. These are dangerous times. You might have to run for your life.'

'And if our side prevails?'

'It is a finder's fee,' he said.

I thought, *and it will consolidate my loyalty to you.*

'You better stay here tonight. Have a few hours' rest. I am going to make some calls.'

My room had a bathroom, and I washed my face and hands and brushed my teeth with toothpaste and a finger. I don't remember lying down, and when I woke it was still dark.

I heard a truck pull up outside and got up and walked into the corridor. Two soldiers with rifles and bandoliers of ammunition were standing by the study door. I went in and found the Colonel in uniform, talking on the telephone. Several officers were standing by the desk, obviously waiting for orders.

The Colonel looked up. He was alert but unstressed. He said, 'Travis, you can help. Will you do it?'

'In for a penny, in for a pound. What do you want me to do?'

'Go with the Lieutenant to the airfield. Take your car. A truck with an NCO and twenty soldiers will go with you. Find the gold and load it into the truck. Wait.'

He turned to the officers and gave them a briefing. He had been busy. He believed he knew who the major conspirators were. They were about to be arrested. Officers loyal to the countercoup would soon control the Army headquarters, the Military School, the Central Police Station, and the telephone and telegraph building. The President had been informed and consented to all these steps. The Vice-President had not been told.

'We have the weapons, the incriminating documents, and some of the gold. Soon we will have all the gold. We have the advantage of surprise. There is a good chance that the conspirators will go quietly. Can't be sure, though, coups are chancy things. Don't hurt anyone unless it is absolutely necessary. They are all Paraguayans.'

He turned to me and said, 'Travis, sketch the layout of the airbase and the exact position of the gold. Make sure the Lieutenant and the Sergeant understand. You will talk to the guards. Come up with any story you like about why the trucks and soldiers are there. They may not believe you, but they will be hesitant. If they try to obstruct you, arrest them. Leave five soldiers at the guardhouse. Go to the hangar and load the gold. Then return to the guardhouse and pick up the soldiers. Release the guards. Cut all the telephone wires you can see. Come back into the city as quickly as you can. Park outside the Military School. Questions?'

The Lieutenant shook his head and so did I. I found a table, paper, and a pencil and sketched the layout of the base and the position of the hangar. Then I drew the inside of the hangar and the position of the crates. I explained it to the officer. He was the kind of man who inspired trust. I explained that there were usually only a handful of soldiers at the base at night. Probably they would all be in the guardhouse. If not, we would go about our business. The soldiers with us greatly outnumbered the guard. If we acted quickly, confidently, our numbers would discourage questions. In any case, it was unlikely that any Air Force personnel were involved. If I were them, I would not care what was happening.

The truck was a six-wheeler, the biggest I had seen since arriving in the country. It was capable of carrying the crates, twenty soldiers, the Sergeant, and the driver. It was parked behind my car with the soldiers aboard and the Sergeant standing beside it. We showed him the sketch and explained the plan.

The Lieutenant and I got into my car. The Sergeant rode with the driver in the cab of the truck. I started the car, turned the headlights on, and drove off, with the truck following close behind. We left the city and soon the lights of the airbase were visible.

As coups go, it was agreeably anticlimactic and my part of it was straightforward.

We stopped at the guardhouse, and I entered it with the Lieutenant, the Sergeant and five men close behind. I greeted the Sergeant of the Guard and informed him that we were there to pick up some crates. By a happy chance, both Sergeants knew each other and supported the same football team. The Sergeant of the Guard looked puzzled but not at all concerned. I left them talking football, with the five soldiers and the other guards for an audience.

I drove around to the back of the hangar and was unlocking the door as the truck backed up to it. I decided it was quicker to load all the crates than open them and look for the gold. Twenty-five minutes after arriving at the hangar, we were back at the guardhouse. The Sergeant had used his initiative and climbed up onto the roof and cut the telephone wires.

The first signs of dawn were apparent when we parked at the Military School. I followed the Lieutenant inside and reported to Estigarribia. He told me to supervise the unloading of the crates and their transfer to the building. I was to open the crates, extract the bags of gold, and bring them up to his office. An hour or so later, the cafeteria was littered with open crates and untidy piles of books about the arcane technicalities of aviation, and all twenty bags of gold were on the floor of the office. A detail of trusted men guarded the corridor and a Lieutenant, a Sergeant and two Privates were inside the office at all times.

Telephones rang almost continuously; soldiers came and went. I saw two men brought in under guard, one of them in pyjamas and dressing gown. Both the men looked half asleep and frightened. My lack of sleep was catching up with me and I looked for a quiet place for a nap. I found an unoccupied office with a large sofa, told the Colonel's escort where to find me, went back to the office, took off my shoes and laid down. I was soon sound asleep.

* *

It was late afternoon when an orderly shook me awake and told me that the Colonel would like to see me. When I arrived at the office, Estigarribia and Arturo Bray were sitting down on opposite sides of the desk, looking relaxed. The gold was nowhere to be seen. A bottle of expensive whisky was open on the desk between them, and each held a large glass half-full of the amber fluid.

Estigarribia said, 'I have been telling Bray how helpful you have been.'

Bray looked at me with his cold eyes and said, 'And to think I was going to have you shot.'

The chilling part of this exchange was that I could not tell whether or not he was joking.

Estigarribia said, 'It is all over. The coup attempt was defeated before it got started. And we know all about the plan.'

He held up a thick handful of handwritten pages.

I said, 'They just admitted everything?'

'Arturo can be very persuasive. The coup was about power and money, not about Bolivian ambitions, or at least that was what the plotters thought. The plans were made through a Brazilian diplomat. He said that he represented a group of businessmen, gangsters really, who wanted to smuggle whisky and cigarettes from Brazil, through Paraguay to Argentina. This was credible because immunity from interference from customs and police would have made huge profits possible. The Vice-President is thought to be venal. The plan was for the Junkers to fly into an airstrip near Nueva Germania. You know that the Junkers had its identity erased and there would have been no hint that it had come from Bolivia, when they thought it was coming from Brazil. The cargo would have been transferred to a launch and brought downriver to the Rio Paraguay. Launches come and go on the Paraguay every day, they are a common sight. It would have been easy to tranship the cargo to a truck, and the conspirators would have had the means to plan, pay for, and execute a coup. The President would be deposed, the Vice-President would have become President, and the Brazilians would be free to carry on their trade. Everyone would have been happy.'

'Why did none of them suspect that the assistance was coming from Bolivia and for strategic reasons?'

'There has been a lack of long-term strategic thinking, the cover story was credible, and they were greedy for money or power or both. They believed what they wanted to believe.'

'What will happen to them?'

'Nothing. We have their statements and other evidence. If we publish it the mob would lynch them. And we are confident that they would not have acted if they had realised who the paymaster really was.'

'But they have committed treason.'

Estigarribia was a realist. 'Only because they lost. If we shot everyone who had ever contemplated a forced change of government, Asunción would be a ghost town. Not really, but we Paraguayans have learned to be flexible in such matters. There are some other things I would like to talk to you about.'

I said, 'I see. "Treason doth never prosper: what's the reason? Why, if it prosper, none dare call it treason."'

'That sounds like a quote.'

I said, 'It is. Sir John Harington, in the time of Queen Elizabeth the First of England.'

Estigarribia looked serious. 'This Bolivian Military Attaché who is frightened that his wife will find out he is patronising a whore. Would she help us extract information from him?'

'Possibly. She is a businesswoman, a Uruguayan with no loyalty to Paraguay. She would expect to be paid. She is very angry about the way he was treating her. That would help us.'

'We would pay. We have the funds, and authority from the President to use them to best advantage.'

I said, 'I am going to meet Julia for a drink in the next few days. I will sound her out. How much am I authorised to offer?'

Bray said, 'Do you know how much she makes as a whore?' His tone suggested that he did not think much of women in Julia's trade.

'No, but she dresses well, travels first class, stays in the best hotels, and owns properties in three cities.'

Bray said, 'We need to know everything she knows about this man, his work and home life. Any other vulnerabilities. And we need her co-operation to set up a meeting. He must not know what is about to happen. Give her two hundred gold guineas as a mark of our good faith. Offer her five hundred more for the assistance I have mentioned. Tell her that if we gather valuable information with her help, we will put her on a monthly retainer. Women in her line of work sometimes learn interesting things from garrulous clients.'

Estigarribia looked at me. 'There is one more thing we would like to talk to you about. We would like you to accept a commission as a Captain in the Arma Aérea.'

'Why?'

'You are useful and would be more useful if you had the status and authority of a commissioned officer. The offer includes a new contract for one year, starting today. You will continue to receive your salary and perks from your civilian employment, plus your officer's pay. What do you say?'

'Would my duties include flying?'

'Yes. Our aviators are busy. You have been tactful, and I am confident you will continue to be so. You are keen to help Paraguay prepare for the inevitable. Your RAF service and civilian flying would justify a direct commission as a Major, but that would engender resentment and would be counterproductive. A Captaincy is undeniably appropriate for a man of your age and experience. Even the proudest young officer will not resent serving under you.'

I thought about the proposal. Soon there would be a war. No one was suggesting that my duties would include combat flying, but Paraguay was short of aviators. There would be plenty of non-combat flying but accepting a commission would be one more step closer to the violence of the enemy. Every man wishes he had been a warrior. I had missed the Great War, but I had been a warrior in later, little-known wars. Had I got a taste for it? Was I authentic without more experience of it, without adding more kills to my logbook, to have shot down five enemy aircraft, to be an ace, even if I would not feature in any list of aces? Someone, I think it was the writer James Salter, a fighter pilot in a later war, wrote: *Come now and let us go and risk our lives unnecessarily. For if they have got any value at all it is this that they have none.* When I read that, I remembered my moment of decision all those years before in Estigarribia's office. And Paraguay had been good to me.

I made my decision and said, 'I accept.'

Bray nodded, and Estigarribia said, 'Excellent, have a drink. I will ask Major San Martin to find a uniform and insignia for you. The President knows that you have helped him keep his job. You will be sworn in at the Presidential Palace at four o'clock the day after tomorrow.'

And so, having arrived in Paraguay by chance, and as a simple deckhand, knowing no one and nothing about the country, I became a Capitán Piloto Aviador Militar (Honoris Causa) in the Arma Aérea Paraguaya.

* *

The uniform I had been given fitted well but was worn, so using my officer's pay, I visited a Portuguese tailor. He created the best uniforms I have ever owned. Once, with Sophia looking on, I donned the dress uniform and admired myself in her full-length mirror. I felt I had a martial look, severe but honourable. She burst out laughing and told me I looked like a schoolboy in some comic opera, pretending to be an officer in a fictional army, Ruritania perhaps.

I entered a period of deep contentment. I had found a niche, a job, a home, and a good livelihood. I was valued, felt connected, authentic, and flew regularly. My affair with Sophia was a continuing delight. Every waking moment I thought of her, naked in the languid afternoons and nights we shared. Sophia borrowed a drafting board for me to use, and as each sheet of her pencil drawings was finished, I traced it in ink. The house I would build back home, someday, took shape.

One day I asked her if she was ever disappointed when she saw one of her designs completed.

'Sometimes.'

'What can you do about it after it is complete?'

'A surgeon may bury his mistakes, but an architect can only advise the client to grow vines.'

I laughed and said, 'That sounds familiar.'

'It should be. Frank Lloyd Wright wrote those words, or something very like them.'

The section I owned in New Zealand faced north, catching the sun, even in midwinter. It was surrounded by the native bush, a private place, quiet except for the sounds of the tui and bellbirds. I am writing these words in the house that took shape on those drawing boards.

* *

I was welcomed into the officers' mess at Ñu Guasú and worked and flew without creating any obvious resentment.

The discontent with President Guggiari simmered on, and there was loose talk about another coup, but no one in authority took it very seriously. Having defeated one coup, nobody wanted to think about another one. At least not so soon.

One day a large envelope arrived from Father de Morais. It contained a detailed list of the materials he had located about the Jesuit Reducción of Trinidad. I conferred with the chief archivist at the national archives and the librarian who was working on the Arma Aérea's library, and they told me that Father de Morais' diligence had covered all the books, pamphlets, and manuscripts that they were aware of. The materials were mostly documentary, with no plans and few photographs. My new duties and allowed me to remedy that.

New classes of pilots and observers were in the middle of their training, and the observers were required to navigate on long cross-country flights, and sometimes I was the pilot. I had checked out on the Potez 25, the two-seater that had carried me to Puerto Casado to search for the mysterious F 13. The Director of the Aviation School authorised a training exercise, which would include Trinidad. One crystal clear and windless day we set off. The first checkpoint was San Bernardino on Lago Ypacarai, then on to towns along the Ferrocarril Central del Paraguay, Villarica, Maciel and Encarnación with the observer keeping a navigational log, doing time and distance calculations, providing me with compass headings to fly and estimated times of arrival to each checkpoint. Finally, we arrived overhead the La Santísima Trinidad de Paraná.

I had planned the flight so that we arrived when the sun was at its highest and the ruins cast the smallest shadows. There was a camera mounted in the bottom of the fuselage, pointing vertically downwards, and I flew at exactly 1,000 metres and exactly due east-west, with the clockwork drive of the intervalometer clicking the shutter every few seconds, producing a series of overlapping photographs. At the end of the run, I turned and flew west-east, with the camera taking photographs that overlapped with those from the first run. After that I made identical runs at 300 metres, and then flew back and forth with the observer standing up in his cockpit operating a large hand-held camera, taking scores of oblique photographs, covering the site from every angle.

The plan had been that we would fly directly back to Asunción as soon as we finished, but the grass around the ruins was green, level and inviting, so I landed. We climbed down and strolled around the ruins, the remains of what had been handsome buildings of stone and red brick. Since they had been abandoned in the late 1760s, weather and time had taken their toll, some roofs had collapsed, and flora had colonised many of the ruins. A large tree had taken root in a roofless room on the second floor of a building, and bass relief carvings were still clearly visible on some of the exterior walls, signs of a vanished experiment in theocratic socialism. Thousands of Indians and a few Jesuit rulers and educators had lived here. The rulers instructed and encouraged the ruled to create but not to be original. There were many images carved into the stones. Pheasants, saints, rococo ducks, harps. I had my Leica and photographed the carvings, a font marked *Anno 1720*, and everything the good Father might be interested in.

The big engine in the Potez was usually started by two men, one standing on each wing root and cranking a handle. I had to stay in the cockpit during the start-up so the observer would have to do the work of two men. He climbed up on the left-wing root, inserted the handle, and cranked as hard as he could. The engine fired, the propellor rotated a few times and stopped. I told him to take a break and we chatted as he got his breath back. He tried again, the engine coughed, it looked like it would die and then burst into life. The breathless observer, his face red and running with sweat, climbed into the rear cockpit and sank down out of sight. I took off away from the ruins, did a low circle over them and climbed out on course for home.

A few days later I assisted the student observer in the darkroom. His training included developing his own photographs, making prints, and creating photomosaics. While I was there, I developed the rolls of film I had exposed using the Leica and made prints. The observer rephotographed his mosaics, producing two photomaps: a small scale one from 1,000 metres, and a large scale one from the runs at 300 metres. True north and magnetic north were drawn onto each photomap. One set of those taken by the observer went to the instructors to be graded. Another was archived, and the third was for Father de Morais. They provided a clear, detailed plan of the ruins, much clearer than any sketch map, better than anything short of a surveyor's plan. The photos I took with my Leica showed more details than any published illustrations.

In wartime, such a photomosaic of enemy fortifications would be invaluable to an officer planning an attack. In fact, they might make the difference between victory and defeat, as they would show every machine-gun post, mortar pit, trench, line of barbed wire, and bunker. Without them, because the Chaco was flat, the best an attacking force could do was to have officers climb the highest trees and use binoculars. Not even a quick overflight and verbal report were adequate. Inevitably, the commander would have incomplete knowledge of the defences and many of his soldiers would pay the price of ignorance. The most important use of the few aircraft each side operated was reconnaissance and preventing the enemy aircraft from carrying out reconnaissance.

I wrote my ecclesiastical friend a letter explaining how the materials had been produced, rolled them up, put them in a sturdy cardboard tube, wrapped the tube in oilcloth, sewed it into a linen covering, and wrote the name and address on it in Indian ink.

I sometimes had a drink at a dockside bar, the one with the pig's trotters and pickled onions, and had got to know a few of the skippers of the river steamers. One of them was the good Father's friend. I found his ship at the docks, gave him the parcel, and he promised to deliver it to the Director at Fuerte Olimpo.

My life was agreeable, with many of the ingredients that made it so. Flying, reading, socialising, Sophia. I had a sense that I was on the brink of something important, without knowing what that something would be.

Chapter Eleven
Flying. 30 May 1932

Men make their own history, but they do not make it as they please; they do not make it under self-selected circumstances, but under circumstances existing already …

— Karl Marx. 1818–1883

Life always seemed easier and simpler when I flew. The challenges clearly defined and the reward immediate.

Early in my flying career, when I was learning the basics and building up experience and skill, the necessary concentration meant I could not fully enjoy the sensations of flying, but when I had about a thousand hours in my logbook, I found that I could relax enough to truly enjoy it. The view from above, the sense of detachment from earthly things. Free movement in three dimensions. The satisfaction of flying so smoothly that pilot and aircraft seemed as one.

All the other pilots were busy, so I was ordered to test fly one of the Wibault 73C fighters after an engine change.

Seven of the type had been purchased from France and they arrived in Paraguay in the late 1920s, but one had been lost in an accident. A young pilot tried to impress his girlfriend by beating up her house in a suburb of Asunción. He stalled at low level, the aircraft flicked into a spin and crashed into the street outside the house, killing the pilot instantly and destroying the machine.

The type was obsolescent. But it was a fighter, and this was my opportunity to get another type in my pilot's logbook.

Early one morning I was standing in front of a hangar looking the aircraft over, thinking that it was the ugliest fighter I had ever seen. Some fighters were beautiful, some were businesslike, but this one seemed to be all straight lines as if the designer's brief had included a direction to forget about aesthetics. It was a parasol-wing monoplane with a tightly cowled, liquid-cooled engine of about 450 horsepower.

The mechanics were men who were proud of their workmanship and might be offended if I made a detailed inspection, yet I had learned to do that, as it was an essential safety measure. I spoke to the Sergeant and feigned ignorance of some technical matters and asked him for advice while walking around the machine and the inspection was done without giving offence.

Soon I was strapped in the open cockpit, dressed in overalls and a leather helmet and goggles, sitting on my parachute. I ran my hands over the controls and instruments until I could have found them blindfolded. The wheels were chocked, and four mechanics were waiting to swing the propeller. Usually, the engine was cranked to start but something was wrong, and it would have to be done the hard way. The mechanics pulled the propeller through with the switches off to suck in fuel. They formed a chain of four men with one gripping a propeller blade. I switched on, set the throttle and mixture, said 'Contact', gave a thumbs up, and the mechanics ran to the side, flicking the propeller half a turn. The engine caught and ran with a crackle from its stub exhausts. I let it idle for a few minutes until the engine pressures and temperatures rose to what I guessed was normal.

Two of the men lay across the rear fuselage and I held the stick hard back and increased power, checking the tachometer, oil pressure, temperature, and the magnetos — left, right and back to both, and then pulled the throttle back to idle. I signalled for the chocks to be pulled away and taxied toward the corner of the airfield, using the rudder to swing the tail from side to side, so I could see ahead, past the long nose.

The windsock hung limp, and I chose to take off toward the river. I lined up, checking the rudder and elevators and ailerons for full and free movement and smoothly opened the throttle. I felt and heard the crackle smooth out, felt the slipstream stiffen the rudder and elevator control. Holding the stick forward brought the tail up and I could see directly ahead. The machine became buoyant, lifted itself into the air and began to climb as I made a gentle turn to the north-east.

At about 300 metres, I eased the throttle back a little, checked the instruments and wound the radiator open a bit. After twenty minutes, I was at 3,000 metres and the air was agreeably cool. I could see into the heat haze over Chaco and the clearer air over Eastern Paraguay. The air was smooth, not a tremor in the sky.

I started to explore the handling by performing steep turns and then throttling back and holding height, doing gentle figure of eight turns to learn the low-speed handling. Picking a point to keep straight on, I throttled back and held the stick back to maintain height. The fighter slowed and I felt a buffet as the airflow over the wings started to break away, a warning of the stall, so I lowered the nose, applied power and climbed away.

How would it spin and recover? My technical Spanish was improving but was imperfect and I could not be sure that I had fully understood all of my conversations with the pilots when talking shop. I reduced the power and held height, keeping the nose on a prominent hill, disregarding the buffeting until the nose dropped suddenly, and the Wibault entered a spin to the left. The ground became a blur. After two turns I applied full opposite rudder, centred the stick and eased it forward until the spin was broken and I could raise the nose and apply power and regain height. The next entry was with the rudder and ailerons deliberately crossed to induce a spin to the right, and I recovered after three turns with the nose precisely on the chosen hill.

Aerobatics are useless in combat but give a pilot a good idea of what he can and cannot do with an aircraft, so I spent ten minutes flying through the basic figures, loops, barrel rolls, stall turns. One of the most useful manoeuvres in combat was a simple hard turn, maximum rate, minimum radius. I rolled into the turn, applying full power, pulling the stick back. I felt a little rumble, the brink of a stall, easing off the backward pressure on the stick until it disappeared. I controlled the height with the ailerons, varying the angle of bank. Too steep and I lost height, too shallow and I gained height. The G-forces, two and a half times the force of gravity, pressed me into my seat, my head heavy and difficult to move. Five minutes of these turns told me what I needed to know about how to get the best out of the machine.

I descended and turned back towards the airfield. The windsock showed that a light breeze was blowing from the river, therefore I planned my approach so I would turn into the wind at one hundred metres and aimed for a spot about seventy-five metres inside the airfield boundary. I sideslipped to lose height quickly. There was a tremor, the airflow starting to break up, I eased off a little and it disappeared. I passed over the fence at twenty metres. Straightening out, I eased back on the stick and touched down smoothly, but main wheels first, tail high. I taxied back to the airfield boundary and took off and flew three more circuits and landings, each time touching down in a perfect three-pointer, main wheels and tail skid touching at the same moment. I taxied in to refuel and thirty minutes later I was airborne again.

I worked on my aerobatics until I could fly a seamless sequence, then turned back towards the airfield. I arrived overhead Ñu Guasú to find that the wind favoured an approach parallel to the hangars and other buildings. I dived steeply towards the airfield with the needle of the airspeed indicator almost touching the stop.

I wanted to inspire confidence in the officers who would be watching, without appearing reckless. I flattened out at about 300 metres and flew across the airfield changing direction with smooth, conservative turns. There were no other aircraft in the area, and I climbed to 500 metres, applied full power and dived at a shallow angle, lining up with the airfield boundary before pulling up into a loop, keeping straight on the fence line and wings parallel with the horizon. Losing sight of the ground, I tilted my head back as the machine passed over the top and the horizon appeared above, and then flowed into its usual place as I levelled out at the bottom of the loop. Turning through 180 degrees, I dived from the opposite direction and looped so precisely that, as I recovered, I passed through the air disturbed by my entry.

Reducing power gradually, I descended in a shallow curve and lined up parallel to the line of hangars, aiming to pass over the boundary a little high. I throttled back, crossed the fence in a steep sideslip with the crackle from the exhausts, and descended steeply, flattening out. At the same time, I rolled the wings level and eased back on the stick until the aeroplane settled onto the ground in a three-point attitude, leaving three puffs of dust where the main wheels and the tail skid touched the ground simultaneously. When I taxied in, I saw a small group of officers outside the command building. As I passed them, one of the men smiled and gave me a thumbs up.

* *

In the time free from flying and other routine duties, there was much discussion of what the air war would be like. The Chaco was enormous, and tens of thousands of soldiers would be engaged on each side, but there would only be a few dozen aeroplanes in the war zone at any one time. The main task would be reconnaissance with bombing missions an occasional secondary task. Air-to-air combats would be few and far between and entirely incidental to the primary mission. Most combats would be chance encounters between two-seaters.

With the aeroplanes and aviators utilised to the full, there was no opportunity to practise air-to-air gunnery or air combat manoeuvring, so I organised some substitutes. The first was skeet shooting with shotguns against clay pigeons catapulted into the air in random directions. This provided all of us with a means of developing deflection shooting, aiming to allow for the movement of the target.

I made two model aircraft. One painted blue and the other red. I held classes and explained the principles of air combat. These classes were based on my experience flying fighters, and on a very useful RAF manual on the subject. I described tactical situations, suggesting the optimum response to each. The models were manoeuvred around the classroom by two pupils, and once the aviators got over their embarrassment at playing with toys, they learned useful lessons. The most likely scenario was one of our two-seaters being attacked and flying defensively.

I discovered that one of the French advisers had taught a tactic I thoroughly disagreed with. He said that a two-seater attacked by fighters should dive to treetop level and fly as slowly as possible, with the gunner fending off attacks. It is true that flying just above the ground prevents the enemy from attacking from below, but a steep dive with the attacking aeroplane within range was suicide. And I explained that speed was the best defence. In combat, they should fly at full throttle because the enemy would then have only a small speed advantage and would be compelled to attack from behind, which would give our rear gunners low deflection shots.

We discussed the scenario where both pilots intended to shoot the other down. The manual had much to say on the subject, but it all boiled down to a simple proposition: keep your eyes open, see him before he sees you, think quickly and decisively, get on his tail, stay on his tail, get close and shoot straight. I did not need to tell my pupils that neither side's aeroplanes had armour plate or self-sealing petrol tanks, and the first man to hit his opponent's cockpit or fuel tank would win.

Flying became a bigger part of my work as time went on. Eventually, I was flying almost every day, searching for sites for airstrips up the east bank of the Rio Paraguay and westwards into the Chaco along the rights of way of the railways, particularly the Puerto Pinasco and Puerto Casado, as they were closest to the probable main area of operations.

I helped ground parties lay the airstrips out and produced plans of each one and its surroundings. The flat, featureless nature of the Chaco would always make air navigation difficult, and I produced other plans, noting anything that might assist a pilot flying from place to place. Many of the features were watercourses, full in the rainy season and bone dry in the dry season. I talked to many of the few residents of these regions and noted any fact of value to the Army or the Air Service. I slept in hammocks under thatched roofs and dealt with heat and insects and enjoyed almost every minute of it. I wrote exotic names in my logbook: Concepción and Horqueta, Estancia Castilla and Palo Santo, Isla Poi and Bahia Negra, Isla Taguato, and many others.

My life became simple, straightforward, spare. I flew and usually enjoyed it. I was productive, doing something essential, something that benefited the country that had welcomed me. Most of the time my possessions fitted into a large canvas bag and a bedroll.

I was away from Asunción for a week at a time. At home, the furnishings were the absolute minimum required to get by. A table and chairs, an armchair and sofa, a bed and bedding. A few pots and pans, crockery, and cutlery for two people. Each time I returned to Sophia, and our time together contributed to my sense of contentment. Sometimes we went out together and sometimes I visited my favourite bars and cafés alone, played poker with some success and wished that nothing would change.

One day we were taking a walk when we saw a crowd gathering outside the offices of a newspaper. Cars were stopped in the middle of the street. Several riders, a bullock cart, and many pedestrians were there. A man was passionately addressing the crowd from the balcony of the building. The crowd was noisy, and I could not catch what he was saying.

Sophia turned to me and said, 'It is war, the Bolivians have attacked a Paraguayan fortin on the shore of the Pitiantuta Lake.'

STATEMENT FROM THE HIGH COMMAND

The Bolivians took a Paraguayan checkpoint guarded by seven soldiers and a Corporal, capturing this and one of the soldiers. After the retaking of the Fort Carlos Antonio López (Pitiantuta) by our troops, there has been no news. The advanced line of the forts remains in the power of our troops. From the towns of the interior, offers are received to enlist in the ranks of the Army. The patriotic fervour of the reserve is indescribable. Signed: A. Rojas.

– General and Commander in Chief of the Army and the National Navy. Asunción. 28 July 1932

BOUNDARY DISPUTE! BOLIVIA AND PARAGUAY — FIGHTING ON FRONTIER

The Buenos Aires correspondent of the New York Times *reports that a warlike spirit is prevailing in both countries, and there have been heavy enlistments and heavy subscriptions of money and supplies ...*

– *The Sydney Morning Herald.* 1 August 1932

PARAGUAY LEGISLATURE ORDERS ARMED FORCES' MOBILIZATION AS WAR LOOMS

War clouds lowered over Paraguay and Bolivia as an executive request for mobilization of all the armed forces of Paraguay was approved by acclamation by both the Chamber of Deputies and the Senate. With popular excitement high, Vice-President Emiliano González Navero transmitted the recommendation for immediate mobilization, including the reserves, and approval was considered certain in advance ... A state of siege was declared throughout Bolivia on July 21 as a result of anti-Paraguayan demonstrations arising from popular excitement over the boundary dispute ...

– The Tribune. 3 August 1932

Chapter Twelve
A Battlefield. 30 September 1932

No matter what orders I give, men will die.

— José Félix Estigarribia

*FIERCE FIGHTING IN EL GRAN CHACO —
BOLIVIANS' DEFEAT REPORTED*

*A report from Asunción, Paraguay, says that Paraguayan forces, fighting
a three-day battle with Bolivians at Fort Boquerón, in the El Gran Chaco
region, completely annihilated the Fourteenth Bolivian Infantry Regiment, and
were meeting with further successes as the fierce battle continued …*

— *The Sydney Morning Herald*. 14 September 1932

TROOPS TRAPPED IN TRENCHES

*(Asunción.) An army communique issued last night announces that
Paraguayan troops have taken 100 yards of Bolivian trenches in the El Gran
Chaco region, 72 Bolivians being killed. This is the first definite announcement
of casualties in the two weeks struggle for the possession of the strategic Fort
Boquerón.*

— *Daily Telegraph*, Sydney. 24 September 1932

COMMUNIQUE NO. 30

*At this moment, the following message is received from the Comandante
Estigarribia: 'When my troops broke the third line of enemy defence this
morning, the occupants of Boquerón surrendered. We took prisoner: Lieutenant
Colonels Marzana and Cuenca, Majors Bravo and Britos, Captains Romero*

and Salinas, numerous officers and 1,000 soldiers, 6 cannons, a large quantity
of armaments and ammunition. I will send more details.'
— Paraguayan Army. General Staff. 29 September 1932

At first, I thought I was looking at a lake, its beautiful surface rippling gently in the breeze, the sun reflecting off the vivid blue surface of the water. As I watched the water seemed to boil and steam. Miniature tornados formed and drifted back and forward. A smoky haze formed a few metres off the surface. Countless millions of butterflies were drinking from the decomposing bodies of those killed in the battle at Fortin Boquerón.

David Atten was standing beside me. He took refuge in his métier and said, 'One day I was in a pass in the Andes and butterflies were pouring through it at the rate of a thousand a second. It went on for days, at least a thousand *every second.*'

When I was growing up, my father's library was my favourite place, and my favourite books were a set of *Battles and Leaders of the Civil War.* They were large volumes and packed with accounts of the American Civil War by the men who fought it. Two of those men made simple statements about the nature of war, and I remember them vividly because I have found them to be true. Confederate General Nathan Bedford Forest said: *War means fighting, fighting means killing.* Union General William Tecumseh Sherman wrote: *You cannot qualify war in harsher terms than I will, war is cruelty, nothing can refine it.* My first visit to a battlefield in the Chaco was a gruesome reminder of the truth of those statements.

The attacks on the fortin had been made after an inadequate reconnaissance, and knowledge of the defences had been purchased with many lives.

Some of the bodies were those of the first wave of the first attack, ten days ago. Others had died yesterday, in the assault that finally broke through and caused the emaciated survivors of the garrison to surrender. Arturo Bray was the first senior officer to enter the fortin and accepted the Bolivian commander's surrender. The surrender marked the first major victory of Paraguay in a war that no one guessed would be fought for almost three more years.

We walked amongst the dead, on a battlefield now silent, cloths soaked in disinfectant over our mouths and noses. I wondered, *does it do the dead any good that they died in a victorious battle, are they any less dead?*

The frontline was a mess of shell holes, tangles of barbed wire, shattered cannons and machine guns, the detritus of war. Clusters of butterflies marked the unburied dead. A large Paraguayan flag flew from a high flagpole in the centre of the fortin.

A few weeks before, I was on the docks at Asunción as soldiers had boarded the gunboats, on the first leg of their journey to the front. They had smiled for their mothers and fathers, their friends and fellow citizens, and the newsreel cameras. It seemed likely that some of those smiling soldiers lay dead around me.

The news of the Paraguayan victory at Fortin Boquerón was reported on the front page of all the newspapers. On the front page of *El Liberal*, there were huge headlines and photographs of the dense crowds that had taken to the streets of the capital to celebrate. Although Estigarribia was only a Lieutenant-Colonel, his name was in large letters across the centre of that front page.

James Gibson had watched with me as the gunboats pulled away from the wharf. He was an English veteran of the Great War and had said, 'They smile because they have grown up hearing about the selfless heroism of their country's soldiers in the War of the 70. They see only glory, I see only their corpses, dead on the barbed wire.' He declaimed:

'Good-morning, good-morning!' the General said,

When we met him last week on our way to the line.
Now the soldiers he smiled at are most of 'em dead,
And we're cursing his staff for incompetent swine.
'He's a cheery old card,' grunted Harry to Jack,
As they slogged up to Arras with rifle and pack.
But he did for them both by his plan of attack.'

I said, 'Siegfried Sassoon, "The General", 1918.'

He nodded. The gunboats were out in the Rio Paraguay. We watched them turn north and disappear.

The Battle of Boquerón had lasted almost three weeks. Bolivian attempts to break out or to raise the siege had all failed.

I was on the battlefield because I had flown the F 13 into an airstrip close by to pick up wounded. David was on the airfield. I don't think I ever found out why he was there. There was a delay, nothing for me to do for a few hours, and we hitched a lift on a truck. We drove past water trucks beside a large well. A chain of men was beside each of them, passing along fifteen-litre tins of water. A soldier sat atop each tank, pouring the water in and throwing the empties down to a second chain who passed them hand-to-hand until they could be refilled. These soldiers were happy, smiling. They had survived or avoided a sanguinary engagement. Some of them might survive the next battle and the next. In a few months or a few years, they would go home. A few kilometres further on, we passed a party of captured Bolivian soldiers, marching toward Isla Poi, their faces impassive, grateful to be alive, wondering what the future held.

Our truck topped a slight rise. I saw a line of white smoke, absolutely straight and kilometres long. Not a fire, rather a regiment of cavalry, invisible beneath the cloud of fine white dust, disturbed by thousands of hooves and drifting away on the sweltering air.

* *

The boys at my high school expected to go off to the Great War when they finished school, and many professed enthusiasm to do so. I had seen wounded survivors of the New Zealand Expeditionary Force and had no eagerness for risking death or mutilation, but I kept my thoughts to myself. The war finished, and instead of the Western Front, I went to a law office and university. And the war had been worse than my worst imaginings.

It is a truism that soldiers who have seen the worst are the least likely to talk about it, and my father was one of those. Our barnstorming tour of the South Island had reached South Westland, and our activities at Whataroa drew a crowd who spent freely in the pub, and out of gratitude, the publican presented my father with a bottle of good Scotch whisky. He was not a drinker, but he liked a good dram. We were camped in a meadow beside the Avro and that night beside our campfire, he told me about his war, something truly sinister.

Now he did not have to go — he was middle-aged, married with children, and had a reserved occupation as the chief mechanical engineer at the Railway Workshops in Dunedin. He talked his way into the Army, was commissioned a Captain and was appointed to the Staff of the New Zealand Division on the Western Front. Sometime in 1918, he was temporarily attached to a Mining Company of the Royal Engineers of the British Army. The mining companies dug tunnels under the German front-line trenches and packed chambers with tons of explosives. The intention was that moments before an attack, the charge was detonated, and it blew a hole in the line. This was intended to help the infantry break through. More often than not something went wrong, the attack was delayed, and the Germans sent reinforcements. Or they countermined, and exploded a charge which destroyed the British tunnel, and everyone in it. The engineers my father was working with had almost finished an ambitious project, including tunnels on several levels. One day the Germans broke into the top-level and pumped in poison gas, which, being heavier than air, filled all the tunnels. All one hundred and forty-seven miners died, asphyxiated in the dark.

I wondered why he had told me the story years after the event, after his years of silence, after talking only in generalities, never about death. He had known some of the men who died in the darkness, deep underground. Perhaps he needed to tell someone. Perhaps he wanted me to know that war is not glamorous, not something to be sought out. Had I sought war? Maybe, maybe not, but I had certainly allowed myself to be drawn into several of them.

* *

I often thought about my father's war and now, at Boquerón, I saw before me my worst fears realised.

Somewhere amongst the dead was the body of a White Russian officer, Lev Shestakov, a charming man with a droll sense of humour, whom I had played bridge with several times at General Belaieff's home. Shestakov had survived fighting the Austria-Hungarians in Poland on the Eastern Front in the Great War and the Reds in Ukraine during the Russian Civil War, only to die so far from his native land.

I had expected that the skirmishes of the last few months would peter out and end in mutual accusations, and complaints to the League of Nations. Now each side had suffered many dead and many more maimed for life, and there were patriotic demonstrations in support of the war in Asunción and La Paz. I had been in Asunción and witnessed the crowds and the flags and the hysteria. I had been to the Chaco, few in the crowd had. I thought, not for the first time, *have they forgotten the reality of the War of the 70? Have they forgotten that few adult males survived that war? Surely a compromise could be reached?* But thousands more would die, then tens of thousands, and each death made it less likely that either nation would settle for anything short of complete victory.

The war had transformed the city of Asunción from a sleepy backwater to one whose streets were packed with soldiers, its docks jammed with ships arriving, loading and departing. Several steamers had been converted to hospital ships and they were kept busy. There was no broadcast radio, so each newspaper installed a huge blackboard on the front of its headquarters and the latest news was chalked on it in huge letters. Each edition of each newspaper carried war news, including communiqués from Army High Command. Not every soldier was keen to go to the green and brown wastes of the Chaco to face certain discomfort and possible death or mutilation. A man of military age dare not appear in civilian clothes, and well-connected families sometimes used their influence to ensure that their sons were commissioned and assigned duties shielding them from service in the combat zone. Amongst the barefoot conscripts were officers in tailored uniforms, whose duties kept them in the cities. These officers searched diligently for deserters whose punishments included immediate dispatch to the Chaco.

Bolivian prisoners taken at Fortin Boquerón were marched through the streets of Asunción while thousands of men and women watched. The prisoners were emaciated, their uniforms torn, and many barefoot. The mothers of Paraguayan soldiers had expected to see monsters but saw only young men, indistinguishable from the sons they had sent to the war. The women took their names and promised to write to their mothers, girlfriends, or wives, to let them know that they were alive.

Supplies and men were being shipped to the Chaco in the gunboats and river steamers, sometimes in strings of cattle barges towed by small tugs, heading north along the Rio Paraguay to Puerto Casado. From there they rode the Casado Railway to the railhead 145 kilometres west at Isla Taguato. There were few trucks, and the infantry marched and the cavalry rode to the base at Isla Poi. I have some photographs before me as I write these words. They are of the young soldiers of an infantry regiment and were taken at Isla Poi as the regiment formed up for the march toward Boquerón and the battlefield. Perhaps some of them were those I had seen boarding the ship. It is striking that the happy faces of a few days before are now thoughtful, some a little scared.

I had spent several weeks planning and supervising the modifications to the F 13 for several different roles and had finished them a few days before the start of the Battle of Boquerón. When news of the fighting arrived, I was ordered to fit the stretchers and fly to the Army's base at Isla Poi.

A few trucks brought wounded to the base, the rest had to endure litters fitted to mules, one each side of the beast, and many of them did not make it and were buried along the way. For a week I flew wounded from Isla Poi to Casado, where they were loaded onto hospital ships to be taken downriver to Concepción or Asunción. I was the only pilot available, and I flew all day and worked unloading and loading at each end of each flight. Sometimes there was no one to refuel the aircraft and I did that as well as attend to minor maintenance. The heat was stifling, and the insects kept me awake. Skirmishes continued after the battle and there was never a shortage of wounded.

Once I flew a badly wounded officer to Ñu Guasú, landing at night along a line of goosenecked flares. I called Sophia and she drove out to the airfield. We talked and I went to sleep in her arms, across the front seat of her car. I was airborne before dawn, bound for Isla Taguato, with the stretchers folded up and stowed. Six officers and their luggage were jammed together in the cabin.

No cargo space was ever wasted and there was always a load to carry from Casado to the zone of operations, once it was a radio, aerials, and dry-cell batteries, on another flight it was telegraph wire for Isla Taguato.

At Casado one morning, I noticed young soldiers entering the church. I followed them and chatted to the Padre. He said, 'Come with me.' He led the way up to the belfry and pointed to the bell. I ducked under it and saw scores of names and dates inscribed on the inside. The Padre said, 'When they come back, if they do, they will write the date of their return.'

COMMUNIQUE. No. 52

The Command of the 1st. Army Corps reports that yesterday it had a short and brilliant action. Our troops took Fortin Fernandez, the enemy fleeing in disarray towards Plantanillo. An important consignment of military effects and food items that the Bolivians had in the said fort was collected. It also communicates that, between Yayucubas and Plantanillo, a patrol of our cavalry attacked a convoy of trucks that were driving enemy troops, causing 39 casualties, and setting a truck on fire. In the Nanawa sector, our forces have engaged in a fierce encounter with the fortified Bolivian troops in Samaclay and Murgia, taking three important lines of positions from them, cutting the telephone network of a thousand metres of wire, more or less ... and causing the enemy considerable losses.

– Paraguayan Army. General Staff. Asunción. 31 October 1932

* *

Water was the key to victory and soldiers dug wells or worked to deepen them while water trucks filled up and drove off toward the front. One day at Boquerón, I saw details of soldiers carrying water to their resting comrades. There were individuals draped in a dozen or more full water bottles, two soldiers were supporting a stick with thirty full water bottles suspended from it. The Paraguayan Army had built its main base at Isla Poi because it was the closest source of large quantities of drinkable water to the battlefields of this early stage of the war. The water was as important as the men, arms, and ammunition.

One evening I played cards with an Argentinian war correspondent, and he pointed out the irony that without the means to drill for water and water trucks to take it to the troops, there could be no general war in the Chaco. Without these trucks, only small numbers of troops could operate, and they had to stay close to the water. Without modern technology, the conflict had consisted of skirmishes, a handful of dead from time to time, and much sabre-rattling in La Paz and Asunción. The availability of water and canned food enabled large numbers of troops to move and fight in much of the disputed area.

* *

One day the engine of the F 13 gave trouble, and I was grounded for two days at Casado. Mechanics worked on it, and I rested while they worked. Trains with boxcars and flatcars full of wounded were arriving every day and the facilities were overwhelmed. The trains stopped in a siding several hundred metres from the wharf. There were no trucks and the stretchers had to be unloaded and carried to the wharf, with four soldiers to each stretcher. As I watched, soldiers struggle to hand a stretcher down to the waiting stretcher-bearers. They almost dropped one and the wounded man screamed. On the wharf, the wounded lay, unprotected from the sun, until they could be loaded onto the waiting hospital ship. The ship would not depart until it had a full load, and it was taking a long time to unload the wagons and load the ship. The soldiers and the doctors and nurses from the ship did their best, and swift transport to hospital care gave the wounded their best chance. But men who had survived the journey from the fighting to the wharf were dying within sight of their salvation.

After two nights of rest, I was fresh and keen to get going. I went back to the wharf and tried to think of something that would speed up the handling of the wounded. As I watched the wounded being unloaded, I saw a man writing in a thick ledger. Despite the heat, he was dressed in a tweed suit and bowler hat. An army officer came by, one I knew by sight. I asked him what the man was doing.

The officer said, 'He is the assistant manager, and he is counting the wounded so that the Casado Company can bill the Army for their transport from Kilometre 145 to here.'

I said, 'They charge the Army, but these boys were wounded protecting the company's lands and forests?'

'Yes, they do. So much for a boxcar of soldiers going up to the fighting, so much for each officer, for each nurse, so much for each wounded man coming back. So much for each wagon of food, ammunition, medical supplies.'

'How much does the Army charge the company for each dead soldier, for each maimed boy?'

My friend shrugged, concerned but helpless. 'It does not work that way.'

'Why doesn't he delegate the job to a clerk?'

'He is an accountant; numbers are important to him.'

An Argentinian volunteer doctor, Carlos de Sanctis, was in charge of the transfer and had been working night and day, with bad food, little rest and in the heat and humidity. He appeared to be out on his feet. The other doctors and the nurses appeared to be just as tired.

I was fresh and alert and could see what they could not — a way of speeding up the process and saving lives. I made some sketches and buttonholed the good doctor in the mess hall and outlined my ideas, and I showed him the sketches. He agreed that my ideas would work but that he could not take the time to make it happen.

I went back to the wharf and saw the man with the ledger. I introduced myself. He told me his name was Llewellyn Jones, although I doubted that he had ever been out of Paraguay or spoke English, let alone

Welsh. I told him who I was and what I wanted to do and what assistance I would need. I told him that Doctor de Sanctis approved.

Jones said, 'You need to talk to the manager. He is in Asunción, back in a week or two.'

'It can't wait a week or two, it must be done now. Are you his assistant?'

'Yes. Write to our head office in Buenos Aires. If they agree I will prepare a quote for the work and send it to Army Command in Asunción.'

'But it needs to be done now, boys are dying now.'

'Can't do it without a signed and stamped work order.'

He grunted and went back to counting the boxcars and their cargo.

I remembered the way these companies treated their workers and the Indians, and the massacre at Pinasco came to mind.

I walked slowly back towards my billet, thinking about the problem. I was wearing civilian clothes, so I changed into my officer's uniform, complete with a cap, Sam Brown belt, pistol, and holster. I went to the command post. The duty officer was someone I was on nodding terms with. He was tired, just like everyone else in this particular nook in hell. I explained what I wanted to do. I did not demand; I was courteous and persuasive as if I were talking to a jury.

He listened and said, 'The Casado Company is powerful and politically well connected. The Command might have you shot. Might have me shot.'

We discussed the matter, and finally he agreed to assign a section of soldiers to help me, and to make more available later if they were needed. I explained that I wanted a particular type of soldier. He laughed and agreed. Soon I was talking to a Sergeant named Garza who was in charge of my detachment. He had a livid and barely healed scar across his face, from one of the early skirmishes. He and his five men were all over 1.85 metres tall. They were armed with rifles, had bandoliers of ammunition across their chests, and each carried a large and very sharp machete. They also looked more Indian than Spanish or Mestizo. I told them what I wanted them to do. The Sergeant nodded and we went to find the man with the ledger.

I found the assistant manager standing beside a flatcar, still counting and making notes. I walked up and stood facing him, my men standing to attention behind me. One of the men drew his machete and started to sharpen it with an oil stone. The accountant looked more surprised than afraid.

I said, 'The Army has agreed that my plans should be carried out. Now.'

He replied, 'You must go through channels.'

'You are going to assign foremen and labourers to carry out the works, you will make track, wood, and tools available to those men. You will instruct them to carry out my orders and, if I am not there, the orders that Sergeant Garza will give them. If you do not comply, this man' — I pointed to the soldier sharpening the machete — 'will chop your right hand off.'

He said, 'You wouldn't dare.'

I drew the Webley from its holster, pulled the hammer back to cock it and pointed at his head.

'All of those wounded boys have mothers and fathers, some of them are from leading families. I don't think any of those parents would want to punish the men who worked to save their lives. If you fail to carry out my orders to the letter, I will make sure that your name and your actions will be known to the families of every man and boy who dies because of you.'

'I don't have the men you require.'

'Yes, you do. At least five hundred men are working in the factory.'

'But I would have to stop production.'

I turned to the soldiers. Two of them held the man by the shoulders and forearms and a third, the one who had been sharpening the machete, stood facing him and raised the weapon. I took the pen and ledger from Jones.

I said, 'Hold his hand down on the deck.'

This might have been the first time the man with the ledger had had his authority questioned, let alone been threatened with the sort of violence his kind dealt out to their workers. He was a petty god at Casado. He had turned white, and his hands shook.

He said, 'Very well.'

I turned to the Sergeant and said, 'Stay with him. I will be by the wharf. Report to me when he has given his orders.'

The assistant manager and the soldiers departed for the factory.

I found Dr de Sanctis and told him what was going to happen, and he introduced me to the captain of the ship, and I described the new system to him. The Sergeant and his men returned, and we were talking when two large groups of workers arrived. One had tools and the timber I had specified. The others carried rails. The narrow-gauge railway was on the Decauville system, 900-millimetre track preformed into sections, with rails and sleepers already attached. A small team of men could carry each section of track and a simple machine was used to bend the rails to any desired angle. The workers also provided a set of points so the trains could shift from one line to another.

I talked to the foremen, showed them my sketches, and helped mark out the ground with the sticks, line and chalk. The railway extension I had sketched curved to the right until it was close to the river and parallel to it. Another section was laid parallel to the wharf and about thirty metres from it. The set of points joined the two new sections. A train could now be turned parallel to the wharf and then back up through the points.

While the track was being laid, another team was building three ramps alongside the section of track closest to the wharf. My confrontation with the accountant had taken place at about eight in the morning, and by five in the afternoon, the ramps and the railway were complete. The train still had wounded aboard, and in a few minutes, it was in the siding. Beside each of the last three wagons there was a ramp, and now each stretcher could easily and quickly be lifted and carried down the ramp to level ground. When those three wagons had been unloaded, the train backed up to put the next three wagons beside the ramps. The good doctor had worked out a plan with the ship's captain. The backlog of wounded was shifted from the wharf to the ship, and a second gangway was dropped to the wharf. The stretchers were carried directly from the wagons, down the ramps and up the gangway to the ship. The returning stretcher-bearers used the second gangway and soon an uninterrupted flow of stretchers was being carried aboard.

By seven that night, the ship was loaded. It drew away from the wharf and turned its bow downstream.

I walked over to the command centre and had a brief message coded and sent to Estigarribia's Chief of Staff:

> *Strongly recommend you immediately telegraph Assistant-Manager at Puerto Casado & thank him and his Company for valuable improvements to the handling of wounded & follow up with letter & copy to Casado Company Head Office, Buenos Aires. Will explain.*
>
> - Capitán C. Travis. Telegram. 1 December 1932

I did not think I would hear any more about my interaction with Llewellyn Jones. To complain, he would have to admit things no sensible man would wish to admit — that he was preoccupied with invoicing the Army and had obstructed the passage of wounded men, and that he had been intimidated by a foreigner and by some Indians. He was probably the kind of man who thought of Indians as his racial inferiors. And I had given him some kudos with the Army and his superiors.

I am prouder of the work I did that day than any other thing I have done in my life, more even than my conduct in the battle in which I would soon fight.

COMMUNIQUE NO. 69

On Sunday at 7 am a Potez aircraft, piloted by Captain Trifon Benitez Vera and Captain Ramon Avalos Sanchez as an observer, flew over the enemy positions in Saavedra. It did not return to its base, and it is known from statements made by prisoners that it fell in the vicinity of that fortress, injuring its crew. (These statements contradict an announcement of the Bolivian command that reported the instantaneous deaths of said officers.) The prisoners add in their statements that the Paraguayan artillery causes destruction in the Bolivian ranks. In the sector of the Fortin President Ayala (Nanawa), our attack caused heavy casualties to the enemy. A Bolivian officer was captured and 4 machine guns and 80 rifles were taken.

– Paraguayan Army. General Staff. 7 December 1932

COMMUNIQUE. No. 75

This morning at 11 am, three enemy planes bombed Bahia Negra, causing the death of Colonel D. José Julian Sanchez, and slightly wounding three soldiers. There is no news from other sectors.

– Paraguayan Army. General Staff. 20 December 1932

Chapter Thirteen
Buenos Aires. 12 January 1933

I was suddenly taken off flying and given a task that required me to sleep between clean sheets, eat meals prepared by a chef, and relax close to a well-stocked bar.

I had flown the Junkers almost every day, and sometimes at night, for several months, the only rest days were when the weather prevented flying. I remembered one of the German pilots telling me the difference between flying weather and flyer's weather. In the combat zone, flyer's weather was when conditions were too bad to fly, and it gave the aviators a rest. After about 350 hours of operating in the heat and dust, the engine needed changing. It was tired and I knew how it felt. There was no replacement engine available, so the Junkers was pushed into the corner of a hangar at Ñu Guasú until one could be found. I was given a few days' leave.

Sophia had volunteered in a hospital and had not had a day off for months. There was a lull in the fighting and few wounded were arriving, so she arranged days off and we spent them together and did not leave her apartment. Sometimes we lay together on her bed. She would trace my scars with a fingertip but didn't ask for a more detailed account of their provenance. If I didn't want to talk about something, she let it drop. I did not like to think about how I had got some of those scars. Finally, we ran out of food and went out to shop. Already there were parties of Bolivian prisoners in their striped prisoner of war uniforms at work on the docks and around the city. Most had the dark skin and features of the natives whose homes lay in the cold, quiet air of the high Andes. Their expressions were neither happy nor sad. Their imprisonment in this strange hot, moist, noisy place was probably only the latest trial in lives that had always been hard. Their tasks here were no more onerous than labouring on hardscrabble farms or the tin mines at home.

Although the interlude was a time of contentment, I remembered something my father had told me. Soldiers sometimes missed their comrades so much that they returned early from leave. I was starting to understand why. I had not flown in combat but every day I saw the consequences of the war I had stumbled into and grew closer to the men I served with and could not avoid empathising with them.

After my few days off, I started flying again, in whatever aeroplane was available on the day. The Air Force had one Curtiss Falcon, a two-seat bomber, and it was converted to a transport. The armament was removed. Two seats were installed in the rear cockpit and a hinged canopy covered those seats. The Falcon was more powerful and faster than the smaller aeroplanes and much in demand. Mostly I flew VIPs to the front and back, once it was Dr Benjamin Banks, Minister of Finance, and twice it was President Eusebio Ayala. So I flew on, eating bad food, always dusty and dirty, often sleeping under a wing or in a hammock, sometimes tormented by insects.

Then my new orders arrived.

I had barely shaken the dust from my uniform when I found myself again in the salon of SS *Miranda*, dressed in a civilian suit and chatting to Julia as the ship left the dock at the Port of Asunción and set off down the Rio Paraguay towards Buenos Aires.

Julia had agreed to help blackmail the Bolivian Military Attaché into betraying his country. Acting on Estigarribia's instructions, I had met with her, given her the good-faith gold, and proposed that she help me. She agreed, for a substantial fee. My contact had been reassigned to Army

Intelligence and the operation was on the books but known to only a few. In the background, but always in my thoughts, was the war.

> COMMUNIQUE NO. 88
>
> *In the President Ayala sector (Nanawa), patrol encounters continue to take place. There is no news from other sectors.*
>
> – Paraguayan Army. General Staff. Asunción. 14 January 1933

> OFFENSIVE, GENEVA INFORMED
>
> *The* Daily Mail*'s Geneva correspondent says that the Paraguayan Government in a note to the League states that it intercepted a wireless code message from General Kundt, ordering the 4th and 5th Divisions of the Bolivian Army to be ready to take the offensive against Paraguay.*
>
> – *Auckland Star.* 25 January 1930

The plan to obtain information from the Bolivian had been deferred because of the outbreak of war, but not forgotten. It had too much potential to let the opportunity pass. I met with Intelligence when time allowed and had several meetings with Julia. It was decided that she would initiate contact with the Attaché and pretend that all was forgiven. She negotiated a handsome retainer and went about her work while it was decided how to use the contact.

I had come to realise that the Paraguayans had an efficient Intelligence Service.

A few years before full-scale fighting broke out in the Chaco, Bolivia had been embarrassed internationally when codebreaking had revealed its plans for an aggressive move in the Chaco. Or the information could have come from a source, highly place in La Paz, and the codebreaking was a cover story to protect the source. Either way, Paraguayan Intelligence was producing valuable information.

The original intention was blackmail to create a well-placed source. But the relationship could be used in several other ways. The Bolivian knew that his paramour frequently travelled to Paraguay, had many friends there, and might hear things of value to his country. It followed that Julia could feed him misleading information, prepared by Paraguayan Intelligence. She would demand payment and the price for the information would make it more credible. And like so many men, the Attaché liked to seem important and talked too much, so she could garner information from him and pass it back. In amongst the hot air, there might be something useful.

There was a question mark in all this. Julia was Uruguayan and had no reason to be loyal to her employer country. She had Paraguayan friends, good ones, but she had many friends in Uruguay and Argentina too. I had the sense that she was honest, but her regular work was the most mercenary imaginable. She could take our gold and do nothing to earn it. Or she could work for both sides.

If she told the Bolivians what information Paraguay wanted them to have, they could take back bearings from the planted information. If it were that Fortin A was being reinforced, for instance, it would suggest that Fortin B was the focus of operations, that kind of thing. If she told the Attaché what questions the Paraguayans wanted to be answered, this would tell the Bolivians what Paraguay did not know.

Julia was intelligent, well-educated and businesslike. She stayed up with current events and would have no trouble creating false but credible information, supply it to both sides and keep the money flowing indefinitely. The false information would be misleading and worse than useless if acted upon.

I attended several meetings when strategy and ways and means were discussed. It was decided that there was to be no subtlety — the target would be confronted and given the choice of co-operation or ruin. To that end, information was gathered that would convince the target that we knew everything worth knowing about him. The Paraguayan Legation in La Paz had been working on this when they were expelled at the outbreak of war. They provided his birth certificate, the birth certificates of his children and his wife, and their marriage certificate. We knew he was a member of an exclusive golf club and was friends with high officials in civil and military life. They also supplied the information that his wife came from one of the wealthiest families in Bolivia, while his family only had a good name. If his wife found out that he had been consorting with a whore for years, he would be pauperised and might never see his wife or his children again.

It had been decided that photographs and voice recordings should be obtained before confronting our target. The recordings aimed to capture unflattering references to his wife, something we had been told was common. If he belittled his superiors, all the better, and if we caught him being indiscreet about his work, better still.

The plans had been finalised. I was on my way downriver, a surreal pleasure. After the sights and smells of the battlefield and the bizarre sight of those millions of butterflies, I had flown scores of seriously wounded soldiers. The memory of those men and the stench of blood, corruption, urine and faeces was always in my mind. Some of my passengers died only a metre or so from me. They called for their mothers in Spanish or Guarani. Once I recognised a plea in Latin, once in Arabic. One day the war came to me. I was loading wounded at Isla Poi when a small formation of Bolivian aircraft bombed and strafed. There was minor damage to two of our aircraft, and a small store of petrol cans was set alight. I was temporarily deafened by a bomb and the aircraft I was hiding under was covered by earth from the blast. It was an event that would not get into the history books, but one of the mechanics was wounded by splinters. He had to have a leg amputated and was sent home to live out his life as best he could.

But now I enjoyed the sensation of clean sheets, the release from the dust and heat and the proximity to death. I took showers that lasted half an hour, sat idly in the bar drinking cocktails. I played cards and did not care that I lost. I met a woman who owned a business producing haute couture in Santiago, the capital of Chile. She had been in Paraguay negotiating with retail stores. There were things the war would not change. The poor would never be able to afford her wares and the wealthy minority always would. She was well read and tall, not beautiful but attractive and interesting, closer to forty-five than thirty-five. Her age was one where the quality of life is as important as years in the ageing process. She was wealthy, relaxed, did not smoke, drank little, had servants to look after her at home. We chatted at the bar; her thigh was warm against mine; her interest clear.

Sophia had made it plain that she liked me but that she was not a one-man woman. She was spending a few weeks with a friend from Rio; she had not said if it was a woman or a man. The tall woman's warm hand migrated to my right thigh. My default position is to never engage with more than one woman at a time. The tall woman's hand slid around to the inside of my thigh. I reconsidered my position. We left the bar for her cabin and did not emerge until the ship docked.

* *

I felt relaxed and content when I disembarked from the ship in Buenos Aires. I had thought that espionage would be exciting, but before long I found that it was rather pedestrian.

In Buenos Aires, I was introduced to the man I would work with. We did not meet at the legation. Argentina was sympathetic to the Paraguayan cause, but it would not do to be caught spying in a friendly nation's capital. The man was an Argentinian private investigator of proven discretion and ability. If he was caught, Paraguay would deny that he was working for them.

The Major's trysts were always on a Wednesday afternoon, and several days before the next one, the detective and I went to set up. Julia owned the neighbouring apartment and had kept it vacant for our use. I watched with fascination as the detective installed himself in a room that had a common wall with Julia's bedroom. His equipment included a Leica camera with several lenses. He also had a Poulsen telegraphone magnetic wire recorder, the first I had seen. The photographs were to be taken through a small hole drilled in the wall. Another hole was prepared for the wires from the microphone to the recorder. The detective went into the bedroom of Julia's apartment and connected the microphone to the wires.

Julia arrived, inspected the handiwork, and we set about testing the equipment. She and I sat on her bed and talked while the detective remained next door with the recorder running and took some photographs while we listened for the shutter. We couldn't hear it, or the recorder. Fortunately, the client liked his sex in the afternoon with the curtains open, so a fast shutter speed could be used and clear images could be obtained, even when there was movement.

In the evening I reviewed the test photographs and sound recordings. The photographs were crisp and clear, and the sound quality was adequate. I asked the detective a question. 'Do you enjoy this?'

'Photographing people having sex?'

'Yes.'

'Tomorrow I will spend hours sitting in a chair looking, not making any noise, waiting for things to happen, listening to banalities, and watching a prostitute pretend that she is aroused by a man she despises. It is about as much fun as a visit to the dentist or taking a shower with my raincoat on.'

We both laughed. On the Wednesday afternoon, I browsed in bookshops while Julia and the detective went about their work. I met with the detective that evening. He had more than fifty prints, at least twenty of which featured a naked man and a naked woman having sex, and in each of those shots, the face of the Military Attaché from the Bolivian Embassy to Argentina was visible. I had already spoken to Julia, who told me that her client had said several nasty things about his wife, and made at least two derogatory comments about his superiors, although nothing confidential was revealed. All the compromising material was audible on the wire.

I sent a coded telegram to Asunción and the reply was that an officer and two men, in civilian clothes, would take the next steamer to Buenos Aires. I was instructed to wait for them. In the meantime, I took a ferry across the River Plate to Montevideo to follow up on some information about aircraft, engines and spares that might be available.

My contact was a Major in the Air Service. When I visited the airfield that was their main base, I found they operated French-built Nieuport 17 and Spad XIII fighters, leftovers from the Great War and, even by the standards of 1932, ancient. The Major noted my interest and I told him I had read about these craft as a boy and was fascinated. He examined my documents, took me for a check flight in a Morane-Saulnier and let me fly both types. An unexpected pleasure and two more types in my logbook. I was in animated conversation with the Major about the delights of flying such aircraft when a pupil ground-looped a Morane and it went over on its back, bringing flying to a halt.

All the aircraft I inspected turned out to be old and in poor condition. Paraguay already had a dozen or so old aircraft, some leftover from the Civil War of the 1920s, and did not need any more. There were some new instruments and an engine. I had done my homework and discovered that the engine would fit the F 13 without any modification to it or the F 13. And it was slightly more powerful than the original one. It was not new, but its logbooks were up to date, and it had been inhibited and stored in a crate in the back of the hangar. It was likely that it would last for five hundred or so flying hours. The purchase was quickly concluded, and I arranged payment and for the instruments and the engine to be shipped to Ñu Guasú.

I returned to Buenos Aires. My other business was with Fritz Sauber, the German pilot I had met on my last visit. A few weeks ago, I had received a telegram from him. His employer had gone broke, Fritz was out of a job and a Waco was for sale. The aeroplane was exactly what Paraguay needed. They also needed experienced pilots, so I asked for and received authorisation to make him an offer of a twelve-month contract, inspect the aeroplane, make an offer for it, and pay Fritz a modest finder's fee if a purchase went ahead.

At the airfield, I inspected the paperwork and found it in order, spoke to the mechanics who maintained the craft, and flew it with Fritz in the right-hand seat. The lawyer for the failed company accepted my offer, Fritz accepted the offer of a contract, and I paid him his finder's fee. By the time I had done all of this, the officer and his men had arrived from Asunción. The officer wanted to act quickly. I introduced him to Julia, they reviewed the materials and decided that Julia would tell the Bolivian that she would be out of town on their regular day, and would he like to meet before then?

I hoped they would make sure she was protected. I asked the Paraguayan officer to make it clear to the Attaché that if Julia were harmed in any way, his superiors and his wife would see the photographs and hear the recording. This would be a bluff because the source would be too valuable to discard over the death of a whore. I told Julia this on our journey downriver. She just laughed and told me she could handle him. I hoped she was right.

Fritz invited me for a night out. He had never been to Paraguay, had heard it was the back-of-beyond and wanted one last night in the bright lights of the big city. The next day was gloomy with low cloud and rain when we departed on the flight to Ñu Guasú. I flew while Fritz lay across the rear seats and tried to sleep off a crippling hangover.

* *

When I arrived back home, I found that every serviceable combat aeroplane was in the war zone. The maintenance group worked day and night to carry out routine maintenance, repair battle damage, and send the aeroplanes back where they were needed.

A shipment of flying clothing arrived from Italy, and I contrived to be issued with a winter weight set and a set for summer. Being Italian, they were stylish as well as being functional. I had given some thought to how to prepare for survival in the event of being forced down in the Chaco. One of the mechanics had been a saddle maker in civilian life, and I negotiated a price for what I needed him to make. The first was a shoulder holster for a pistol and spare magazines, the other was a survival pack with the essentials. The pack would clip onto my parachute harness, and I made sure that all my gear would remain attached during the shock of a parachute opening. I was in my office trying on all my new equipment when Sophia arrived to pick me up. Usually, she would have teased me about playing warrior, but she had come from a hospital full of wounded. She just looked serious, and said, 'Dressed to kill?'

New aircraft had arrived and the crates containing them were about to be opened. There were seven French two-seat Potez 25TOE reconnaissance bombers, improved versions of the ones already in service, and five Italian Fiat CR20bis single-seat fighters. The engines in the Wibaults had not coped well with the heat and dust of the Chaco and two had been lost in accidents. The Fiats were more advanced, and we hoped more reliable. I pitched in and helped assemble the aircraft and did some of the test flying. We worked on one aircraft at a time and soon we were able to assemble and test an aircraft each day.

The Potez had a deeper forward fuselage, greater fuel capacity, and a stronger undercarriage than the earlier models. The assembly was straightforward, and I flew one on its test flight and found that the handling was unchanged.

Assembling the Fiats was a challenge, as we only had the manufacturer's handbook and common sense to go by. A technical note from the library told us what to expect when we tested them.

FIAT CR20 PURSUIT AIRPLANE

The new Fiat CR20 pursuit airplane, with four machine guns, has the best military, aerodynamic, and static characteristics yet attained … The engine is a 12-cylinder V Fiat A20, with a normal HP. of 410 at 2100 RPM. The fine qualities of the airplane are due largely to the excellence of the engine, which represents the last word in engine building … The armament consists of four machine guns, all located in the fuselage, two, which fire through the propeller, being conveniently situated near the pilot … The ammunition boxes are on the sides and under the engine cowling, suitably protected. The total ammunition consists of about 2000 cartridges … Special attention was given the matter of visibility, the pilot being seated high with reference to the top of the fuselage, thus affording him an ample field of vision both above and below the upper wing … The whole airplane has such a compact form as to make the moment of inertia very small in all directions, thus giving it great manoeuvrability and enabling it to perform all kinds of acrobatic stunts.

– National Advisory Committee for Aeronautics. *Aircraft Circular No. 43. Fiat CR20 Pursuit Airplane.* 1927

The Fiat was a compact biplane with unequal span wings, unusual V-pattern interplane struts, and a businesslike appearance. And it was fitted with a clever system to make starting easier. This was an inertia starter. A ground crew member stood on the left-wing root and operated a crank handle inserted into the engine cowling. As he cranked, a flywheel started to spin and created a rising whine. At a signal from the pilot, he withdrew the handle, reached inside the cowling and pulled a clutch lever. This transferred the energy from the flywheel to the engine which turned over and burst into life.

I flew the fourth and fifth Fiats to be assembled and took an immediate liking to them. The controls were light and well harmonised, and the type was more manoeuvrable than the Wibault and inspired confidence.

One evening I decided to check the speed, rate of climb and ceiling, and set off with a pad, pencil and stopwatch strapped to my right thigh. The top speed was greater, the rate of climb superior, and the ceiling higher than the French fighter. Oxygen gear had been supplied with the aircraft but not fitted. So although it was still climbing at 150 metres per minute at 6,000 metres, I broke off the climb and descended, with some power on, in wide spirals over the river and the city as the sun set. I landed in the last of the evening twilight.

The standard armament of a fighter in those years was two rifle-calibre machine guns mounted inside the fuselage in front of the pilot and firing through the arc of the propeller. The Fiat was supplied with an additional two machine guns and mountings for them, one on each side of the cockpit, but command decreed that the weight and drag of the additional guns outweighed the advantage of extra firepower, and the extra weapons were not fitted.

The guns were fitted with synchronising gears to prevent them from shooting the propellor off and were carefully tested before they were fired in the air. I spent one day working on the guns. Each aeroplane was propped up in the flying attitude in front of a sandbagged wall and the mechanism was tested and adjusted until I was sure it would function in flight. As a final test, the engine was run at full power and the guns were fired at the sandbags.

I had the armourer harmonise the guns so that their fire converged at fifty metres, the norm was more than three times that, but my experience in China had convinced me that a shorter distance was more likely to be lethal.

Chapter Fourteen
A Mission. 25 January 1933

COMMUNIQUE 96

The enemy disaster yesterday was gruesome. In ten minutes of hand-to-hand fighting, Bolivian Regiment No. 41 was destroyed. Until this morning, 225 corpses had been counted and 168 rifles had already been collected, also 20,000 rounds of ammunition for heavy machine guns, spare parts for automatic weapons and 15 boxes of ammunition belts. Recovery of all the weapons of the enemy regiment continues but the work is difficult because the field is covered with tall vegetation. Among the prisoners who have fallen into our power, are Sergeant Nestor Virrueto Garcia, and the medics Adrian Mores and Luis Jauregui, and Lt. Larrera, Commander of the Regiment. There are more Bolivian dead and wounded scattered in the areas where the fighting took place and hidden in the neighbouring forests.

– Paraguayan Army. General Staff. Asunción. 25 January 1933

I was in the mess at Ñu Guasú having a drink after work when one of the Intelligence officers told me that Major San Martin wanted to see me.

San Martin got straight to the point. 'We have a job for you. You will need one other pilot and a mechanic.' He stood up and went to a large map of the Chaco. 'We are building a fortin here.' He indicated a blank area, several hundred kilometres north of Isla Poi, and a hundred or so south-west of Bahia Negra, about twenty-five kilometres west of the Rio Paraguay.

'The bulk of both armies are engaged in the vicinity of Boquerón, and we are expecting another Bolivian offensive against Arce and Nanawa.

Both sides have small forces in the north, to the west of Bahia Negra. We have reason to believe the Bolivians will mount a drive along this axis.' He indicated a spread of territory in the Chaco running north-west to south-east well to the north of Fuerte Olimpo, south of Bahia Negra and ending on the west bank of the Rio Paraguay.

I said, 'They are opening a third front? Why?'

'They have discovered two or three, we are not exactly sure how many, sources of drinkable water in that region. Enough water to support a large force on a march to the river. We have always assumed that that region was uncrossable because of a lack of water.'

'But our Army will be able to attack both flanks.'

'No, it won't. The Bolivians have also discovered that the swath of terrain is flanked by inundations, probably all the year round, definitely for the next few months. No large force can cross either quickly. The Bolivians can move their forces relatively quickly because they are on dry ground. If they discover our troops moving through the swamps, they can easily block them. Entrenched machine guns and mortars on the dry ground would massacre a force struggling through the swamps.'

There was no mystery to me finding out about these geographical features for the first time. I remembered that the Chaco was bigger than England, Scotland, and Wales combined and was still largely unexplored.

'But how did our Intelligence know about Bolivian knowledge and intentions? Are you sure about all this?'

'Yes, we have a very reliable source.'

I thought, *I bet you do — the Attaché.*

I said, 'But you can build a line of fortifications across the dry land. They can't outflank it because of the swamps on either end of our line.'

'We don't have enough soldiers to spare. Most of our forces must be in the south-west for the coming battles, and they will be desperate battles. And in the north, we have just about enough soldiers to hold in position. We have scraped up about three hundred and fifty infantry, fifty to a hundred cavalry, some artillery and machine guns, barbed wire, and a large number of picks and shovels. Fortin X is at the narrowest point of dry terrain. It dominates the sides as well as the front. We are building an airstrip. Your detachment will assist the defence in any way you can. We think our position has not been spotted. When it is, the Bolivians will mount an attack with everything they have, and they have a lot more than us. Remember, Bolivia has a population three times ours and we know they have more soldiers and weapons.'

'Why is this so important? There is not much of value there or north of it, or across the river in Paraguay proper.'

His reply was the same, almost word for word, as that which Estigarribia had given me at the time of the countercoup.

San Martin said, 'You know our strategy is to keep Bolivia away from the river?'

'Yes, a few months back Colonel Estigarribia explained why. I imagine the strategy is as important now as it was at the beginning of the war.'

'More important. Because of this third front that must be defended. You know they can isolate our forces in the northern sector, force them to surrender. They will build a shipyard, float sections of gunboats down to it, assemble them, and build up a river fleet we cannot counter. They might build a light railway and bring the sections in that way.'

There was nothing fanciful about the notion that large warships might be assembled on the shores of the Rio Paraguay. Back around 1912 or so, in New Zealand, a large steamer, TSS *Earnslaw,* had been built for service on Lake Wakatipu in Central Otago. It was constructed in Dunedin, then disassembled, and the sections were railed to Kingston at the southern shore of the lake to be reassembled there. The last time I checked, it was still plying the lake. And Imperial Germany had created a fleet on Lake Tanganyika, in the colony of German East Africa, just before the Great War. They brought large steamers to the lake in pieces by railway and assembling them on the eastern shore. When war broke out in 1914, their freshwater Navy controlled the lake, and it was the only way to move large numbers of men and supplies around the war zone. Control of the lake meant control of the shores and the hinterland. It had taken the British and Belgians two years to wrest control of the lake from the Germans. The Royal Navy had finally transported small warships overland to the western shore, an epic journey. Once there, those warships sank or captured most of the German steamers and control of the lake passed to the Allies.

San Martin went on, 'You know we only have two modern gunboats, a couple of old ones, and commercial steamers. If Bolivia controls the upper river, they can cross it, invade Eastern Paraguay and march on Asunción. In the War of the 70, the Triple Alliance occupied the capital until they had forced us to pay a huge indemnity and cede large sections of our territory. That can't happen again. If it does, it is only one more step to oblivion. The issue will be decided by the force at the new fortin, but you may be able to help.'

There was a silence and I thought it through. Nothing was inevitable, this was not win or lose, but if the move was not blocked, a Bolivian victory in the war was more likely. The reverse would be true.

'Why me?'

'You are the only experienced pilot we have available. We can give you the German and Garcia. You can have one of the Fiats and the Junkers, the big one. When can you move?'

'The Junkers is the middle of an engine change. The Fiat will need work. Are the men ready?'

'Yes.'

I thought about it, mentally compiling lists of what had to be done and what equipment we would need. I said, 'You are prepared to trust two foreigners with this mission?'

He smiled and said, 'No choice.'

The only reassuring thing was that at least he was being honest.

'Will I have priority? Here, at Ñu Guasú?'

'We can give you that. All of the bombers and all but one of the fighters are already in the war zones and work in progress can be deferred until you are away. You can have all the assistance you need. And you can have all the petrol, oil and ammunition you can fit in the Junkers.'

'In that case, I will try to get away within seventy-two hours.'

'No sooner?'

'I will try.'

'The longer we can conceal our preparations, the stronger the fortin will be. Don't tell your men where they are going. Tell them that they are on their way to Isla Poi. You will have to refuel at Casado, brief them just before you take off from there.'

I had been briefed on Tuesday night, and just before dawn on Saturday, I was airborne. The Fiat had only done a few flying hours since assembly and was in tip-top condition. I decided that I needed all the advantages I could get, so I had had the two additional machine guns mounted and tested at the butts. This gave the Fiat twice the firepower of any fighter I might meet. While I was at it, I had the reconnaissance camera installed. It was located in the fuselage, just behind the pilot, and took vertical pictures through an open hatch in the underside of the aeroplane. The hatch and the camera were controlled remotely by the pilot. The airframe was silver doped with red, white, and blue stripes in place of the usual roundels. The Junkers had the engine change completed and ground tested; there had been no time to do an air test. I had hoped to fit it with bomb racks, but there were no racks or bombs to spare. There had been no time to camouflage either aeroplane.

I took off first and circled until the Junkers was airborne. I got a thumbs up from Sauber. My cruising speed was faster than that of the other aeroplane, so I went ahead. Clouds filled the valleys far to the east of the river, huge white glaciers bright in the morning sun.

I was on the ground at Casado, talking to the Intelligence officer about the state of the battles down south, when the Junkers arrived. We had to wait for a message that the airstrip at the fortin was ready for us. The fortin had a radio but could not use it because the Bolivians might pick up the message. Messages would be in code, but the problem was they might use a direction finder and realise that it came from a place where no Paraguayan unit should be. The advance party had strung a telegraph line to the west bank of the river, where it was connected to the telegraph system, joining Bahia Negra and southern Paraguay. A Bolivian patrol might tap into the telegraph line, but then they would already know something was up.

The message arrived before dawn. The aircraft were fuelled and ready to go. I took the men aside, opened my map on the wing of the Junkers and briefed them on the situation. They asked a few questions, most of which I could not answer. They both looked gloomy but climbed into the Junkers and soon both aircraft were airborne.

Command was doing everything it could to conceal the preparation of the fortin. The ground force, its weapons, ammunition and supplies had been loaded aboard two river steamers; being told they were reinforcements for the southern front. Only the officer commanding had been briefed. As they approached Casado, the captain of the steamer had been told, as had the officers. They contrived to pass Casado and the ports north of it at night.

After take-off, we turned west along the railway until out of sight of Casado, then angled north-east back towards the river. The morning after my briefing at Ñu Guasú, I had fuel, oil and equipment, including ammunition, loaded on trucks, driven down to the docks and transferred to a steamer, which had set off before midday. Half an hour after take-off from Casado, we passed it. As with the earlier ships, only the officer in command knew the destination and like them, it passed the river ports at night.

I had decided that both aeroplanes would stay together until we arrived at the fortin, and I flew throttled back to match speeds. From time to time, we exchanged messages. This was by zogging, using arm movements to indicate the dots and dashes of Morse code. It was easy enough for me because I could reach down the side of my fighter easily. A short arm movement was a dot, and a long arm movement was a dash. The other pilot was in a semi-enclosed cockpit and could not easily reach down the fuselage. Instead, he had to put his arm half up for a dot and all the way up for a dash. Our messages were mostly for practise. If there was engine trouble or bad weather, we could discuss what to do. Zogging was no use in combat; things happened too fast.

A little over an hour after take-off, I could see a steamer against the riverbank and circled overhead. There was no port, but gangways had been lowered from the deck down to the shore and two sets of planks lead up to dry land. I could see that unloading was back-breaking work. I could also see two trucks being loaded. A water tank for a truck lay on the shore. I had been told that the fortin was about ten minutes flying west of the river, and that I would be able to see and follow a track. The fortin was on the eastern edge of a large, pear-shaped open area.

We turned west, keeping the faint track in sight on our left. The terrain was flat and easy going through meadows and around clumps of palm trees on slightly higher ground. After about fifteen kilometres, the open country turned to thorn forest. A narrow path lay through the thorns, and I could guess how difficult it must have been to cut it through the lacerating forest in the stifling heat and humidity. We flew past a long line of pack mules.

The air was hazy and we came upon the fortin suddenly. It was reassuring that it was hard to spot from the air. I zogged a message to Sauber that I would land first, and he should circle until I could check the condition of the airstrip. It looked long enough and wide enough but it had not been laid out by an aviator, and the ends were not far from the trees. I set up an approach and flattened out at fifteen metres and slightly to one side and inspected the surface as I flew along. It looked adequate, but I was aware that if an accident occurred, neither machine could be repaired. I made another approach and crossed the threshold with some power on, but as slowly as I dared. I flattened out and sank onto the ground in a perfect three-pointer. As the Fiat touched, I chopped the throttle and held the stick hard back. We lurched a little side-to-side, pitched back and forward slightly, and came to a safe stop. I taxied forward into a gap in the thorns and cut the engine. I climbed out and unrolled two wide strips of white cloth. I laid them out in an L-shape, the signal that it was safe to land.

The F 13 circled, set up an approach, landed and taxied up to where I was waiting. A young Second-Lieutenant walked up and saluted. He said, 'We will help you conceal the aeroplanes.'

The soldiers had cut into the thorn forest beside the strip and created a space big enough for both aeroplanes. The upper branches of the trees had not been cut and provided an almost complete overhead cover. I showed the soldiers where to push and both aeroplanes were turned around and moved tail-first into the space. We had some sheets of canvas and pulled them over the windscreens and windows of the aircraft so they would not glint in the sun. I was confident that the overhead cover made them invisible from above.

The Lieutenant said, 'The Colonel would like to see you and the other officer.'

We followed him down into a trench and along to a dugout covered with quebracho logs, with earth heaped on the roof. The officer commanding was a Major with the red facings of the infantry. I saluted, 'Captain Connor Travis.' I introduced Sauber.

The Major gave a tired smile. 'Welcome to our corner of hell. I should have said, "Welcome to *what will be* our corner of hell." Let me brief you.'

At that moment, a Captain with the insignia of the engineers, and a Russian-look about him, arrived and saluted.

The Major said, 'Travis, this is Ivan Vatutin. He has planned the defences and is supervising their construction. This is his third war, so his advice is worth listening to.'

The Captain said, 'It is.'

I assumed that the other wars were the Great War and the Russian Civil War.

The Major turned to a sketch map and a plan of the fortin tacked up on a wall, and he started to outline the position. First, he described the strategic position which was exactly as it had been outlined to me at Ñu Guasú. There were some points I wanted to clarify.

'Do the Bolivians know you are here?'

'We don't think so. Our patrols have not seen them and there has been no sign of aircraft.'

'When are you expecting them?'

'Soon, a week, a few days.'

'Will your fortifications be complete in time? Do you have the men and the weapons to do the job?'

'We have small arms for each man, including rifles, a hundred submachine guns, a battery of eighty-one-millimetre mortars, six heavy- and eight light-machine guns, and plenty of ammunition. And entrenching tools. A lot of this was captured from the Bolivians at Fortín Boquerón.'

He turned to the Russian. 'Ivan, please explain your plan to Captain Travis.'

I said, 'I am an aviator and don't know much about field fortifications.'

Vatutin replied, 'Then I will explain the basics.' He picked up a stick and used it to indicate points on a map of the area and the sketch map of the fortín. 'If they outflank us, they can advance to the river. That means failure and surrender will be inevitable. So, we must have clear fields of fire in front and to the sides to the inundations on each of our flanks. Our front line faces west, and on each flank it turns toward the swamps. We have three belts of barbed wire along the front and the flanks.' He pointed to each machine gun position and the mortar pits.

The lines of trenches had a zigzag every twenty-five metres or so. I knew they were dug like that so if a grenade or shell dropped into a trench it is contained between the zigzags, the traverses.

'The second line is the same. In the first line are machine-gun emplacements, which are sited to cover one another.' He referred to the plan. 'These are communications trenches which link the lines with each other, the command post, ammunition dumps, a hospital, food supplies and water supplies. You can see that all of these are duplicated, that way a single shell cannot destroy all essential supplies or personnel. And we can move all over the fortín without exposing ourselves above ground. Any questions?'

I asked, 'How long will your supplies last?'

'Food for a month, ammunition for two weeks' fighting, six days' worth if the fighting is intense. Water for ten days. We are lucky, we have found a spring about five kilometres east and are bringing in more water every day by pack mules. We hope to have a month's supply before the battle starts. You saw the track?'

'I did.'

'When the fortifications are complete, we will widen the track and use a tanker truck. We will also bring in more ammunition and supplies. If we have the time.'

The Major said, 'If we can hold the Bolivians for a month, the battles in the south-eastern Chaco will be over, or at least there will be a pause, and there will be enough spare men to build fortifications so strong they won't be worth attacking. The Bolivian campaign in this area will wither on the vine. Of course, if we fail, they will reach the river and the Army will have a three-front war. The historians will put a magnifying glass to what we do and may find us wanting. Especially if the outcome proves to be decisive.'

I was heartened by the Major's attitude. He seemed to be one of those officers who did not fear responsibility. You might think that he was a defeatist, but he was just being objective, and he was well liked by his men. He had that indefinable something that made men have confidence in his leadership.

I said, 'How can we help?'

'By being ready to act. The Bolivians' ignorance of our existence is to be maintained as long as possible. It occurs to me that knowledge of the enemy's strength is of limited value. We can't manoeuvre and we will not be reinforced, so we will have to sit and take it. On the other hand, anything you can do to prevent aerial reconnaissance of our fortifications would be valuable. We are taking pains to camouflage everything, and they won't see much from the front. Their only option is to attack and learn the hard way. You have a fighter and a bomber?'

'Only a fighter. The F 13 is a transport. The Fiat is fast and manoeuvrable, heavily armed, and a match for any enemy aircraft we are likely to encounter. Except the Curtiss Hawk II. We don't know if they are in service. The problem is that I may encounter more than one aeroplane. Early warning would help a lot. Can you site observation posts to the west?'

'I am afraid not. Not enough men or time. And they would be too exposed. We have built a treetop platform close to where your aeroplanes are parked. It has an all-around view, and we can easily provide a telephone connection from it to your shelter.'

'That would help.'

Several officers had arrived during our discussion and clearly needed to talk to the Major, who said, 'Vatutin, please show Travis around. Travis, tell Vatutin what you need. Both of you report to me again at eighteen-hundred hours.'

Vatutin said, 'Follow me.'

I found the German, and Vatutin gave us the guided tour. Work was well advanced and would be completed within a few days. The machine-gun posts were reinforced with quebracho logs and had them as overhead cover too, the logs of the roof covered with heaped earth. The vegetation had been replaced on the tops and sides. I inspected the interiors and found that each had a machine gun with a wide field of fire. The posts on each end of the line could sweep the area where the dry earth turned into a swamp. I noticed something unusual and asked about it.

'Why is there a canvas sheet pegged down under the muzzle of each gun?'

'It stops the muzzle blast from raising a dust cloud. The enemy will have trouble finding and targeting the posts.'

One of the posts was equipped with a 20 mm Becker machine cannon. I asked about it.

Vatutin said, 'The Bolivians used it as an anti-aircraft gun. We captured it at Boquerón. The Bolivians have tanks and may use them here. If they do, the cannon should be able to deal with them. We also have an anti-aircraft mounting for it.'

Several of the bunkers were packed with canned food with more in glass jars. The ammunition bunkers had ammunition of all kinds, including scores of boxes of mills bombs, hand grenades resembling small pineapples.

Gunners stripped to the waist were digging pits for their mortars. One of them looked familiar. It was the ubiquitous Alfredo Stroessner. We exchanged a few words and he returned to his digging. He was an officer who pitched in with his men. An officer with the instinctive knowledge of what makes men trust and follow.

When we were out of earshot of Stroessner and his men, Vatutin said, 'That young man is a first-class officer and will do well, if he survives this war.' He paused and went on, 'And he is a cold-blooded one. A few days ago, two Indian families were spotted a short distance away, just looking. We arrested them. They were probably just passing by, but they might encounter Bolivians, who would interrogate them. They would tell the interrogator things we did not want the enemy to know. Most importantly, they would have told the Bolivians that there were many soldiers between them and the river. We don't have the food to feed them or the soldiers to guard them. We dare not let them go. Stroessner made them lie face down on the ground and shot each one in the back of the head. Two men, two women, and four children. One of the children was no more than three years old. A girl.'

After the tour, we were shown a place to lay out our bedrolls and were given some rations. After eating I checked on the aircraft. The F 13 had carried enough fuel to fill the Fiat up twice. The Fiat's ammunition trays were full, and the Junkers had carried enough ammunition to reload the guns twice. The ship we had seen on the Rio Paraguay carried enough petrol for twenty hours of flying and enough ammunition to reload five times. If the battle started before the cargo arrived at the fortin, it would be anyone's guess whether or not the supplies would reach us. It was always possible that Bolivian patrols could outflank us through the swamps and attack our lines of supply.

I could see that a single bomb or shell could destroy both aeroplanes. I went looking for Vatutin and explained the situation. He said, 'How can I help?'

'Do you have empty sandbags and some spare manpower?'

'Yes.'

'Please have sandbags filled and walls built with them in an E-shape, with the openings facing the airstrip. They will house the aeroplanes and protect them from anything but a direct hit. One section must be big enough to surround the Fiat on three sides, and at least two metres higher than the aeroplane. It needs to be wide enough to take the Fiat when it is facing the airstrip and give us free movement around the aircraft. The other bay will house the Junkers and will need to be bigger. I will show the soldiers exactly what I want.'

While the revetments were being built, we refuelled both aircraft and thoroughly inspected them. I had given some thought to the type of ammunition to use and decided on one tracer, one incendiary, one armour piercing, and five ball. Repeated over and over in each belt. A gun that jammed because of defective ammunition was useless. I sat on a canvas sheet with boxes of ammunition and a tool to check the size of each round. Checking them, I discarded any that were not a perfect fit and inserted the rest into belts. When I was finished, we removed the ammunition from the Fiat and replaced it with the belts I had been working on. I repeated the process until all belts contained the load I had decided on, each round checked for fit, and each belt carefully loaded into its metal box, ready for re-arming.

While that was underway, a field telephone was installed and tested. It connected us with the observation post and the command centre. The telephone, and a ladder leading to the observation platform, were placed in one rear corner of the Fiat's revetment; we put our bedrolls in the other. I met with the observers and told them exactly what I needed to know if they sighted an aeroplane.

After resting and eating, we helped to fill and stack the sandbags. By the time we were finished, it was getting dark. We were exhausted. There was nothing left to be done. The others were soon asleep, but I lay wide awake and thinking.

Why had I allowed myself to drift into another war, one so easy to avoid? Not out of gratitude to the country that had given me so much, for I had already done that. I was here and about to risk all because of the indescribable temptation of danger, the fearful pleasure of coming as near to destruction as possible, and to survive.

The air was still and clear, stars twinkling through the foliage above the revetment.

Chapter Fifteen
A Single Daring Act. 2 February 1933

The importance of accurate marksmanship cannot be overstated, since it is necessary to hit an aircraft in a vital spot in order to destroy it and in air fighting only fleeting opportunities occur. The use of explosive or incendiary bullets increases the vulnerability of the aircraft, but the vital area is nonetheless small in relation to the size of the target ... [I]n the air, a pilot's aim is constantly being thrown off and it will therefore be necessary to re-lay the aim frequently and this implies that short bursts only should be fired, the aim being re-laid at the commencement of each burst. ... [I]f a crew member parachutes from a disabled enemy machine, every effort should be made to kill him since trained personnel are more difficult to replace than material.

–Air Ministry. *Air Publication 928: RAF Flying Training Manual. Part II, Applied Flying.* 1922

We were as prepared as we were ever going to be and now endured the mind-numbing monotony of a long wait with nothing to do. I experienced the many inconveniences of a soldier's life on campaign. Nowhere to sit comfortably, no table to eat at, nowhere to hang my clothes, the same food day in, day out.

Early one morning a few days after we arrived, I was woken by the distant sound of gunfire. It went on for several minutes and then there was silence. I dressed and went to the command post. There was no news and we all waited. Hours passed.

A dust-covered cavalry officer arrived and reported that the firing had happened when his patrol had chanced on the Bolivian vanguard. Large numbers of infantry and cavalry, with some artillery, were advancing due east. The Bolivians had appeared to be completely surprised. They now knew that there were Paraguayan soldiers in the area, but not how many and not that there were fortifications in their path.

The supplies for the aircraft arrived and we took picks and shovels and dug two holes, each big enough to hold half of the supplies. We would not lose all our petrol or oil or ammunition to one bomb or shell. And at least it gave us something meaningful to do.

The fortifications were complete, and the garrison was as ready as it was possible to be.

The morning after the skirmish, I awoke cold and shaking. It took me a few seconds to realise that it was because the temperature had dropped radically during the night. Yesterday I had sweated through the usual heat and humidity, today there was a hard frost on the ground, the grass crunched beneath my feet, my breath visible in the still air. The frost gave me a tactical advantage. As long as the ground was frozen, my take-off would not raise a dust cloud. Bolivian aeroplanes would be less likely to spot me.

Before dawn, I was in the shelter checking the Fiat. The tanks were full of petrol and oil, the ammunition bins full, the chocks in front of the wheels. In the cockpit the throttle and mixture controls were set, the seat belts laid out for easy doing up. The parachute sat in the back of the seat with its straps lying on top of the seat belts. My soft leather helmet and goggles were draped over the windscreen. The crank handle was in the inertia starter. Everyone understood exactly what they had to do.

Late in the morning, I was finishing an early lunch when the phone in the shelter rang. Two aeroplanes had been sighted. I told Sauber and Garcia to start the Fiat's engine and wait. I heard the whine of the starter as I climbed the ladder with my binoculars in hand. The aeroplanes were two-seat Curtiss Ospreys, one of the new American types that had just entered Bolivian service. Perhaps a little faster than the Fiat, but not as manoeuvrable, and with a lower rate of climb. One fixed gun, firing forward through the arc of the propeller, and one on a flexible mount for the observer. They were flying at about 1,000 metres in loose formation and on a course that would take them past the fortin a little to the north, towards the river. The gunners in the fortin had strict instructions not to fire unless an aircraft attacked. The aviators had not seen us, but they would probably see the trail and follow it back to the river where a steamer was unloading. They would then know that there was something to find between the river and the advancing Bolivian troops. Once they found it, they would photograph it and create a mosaic with the photos, a map of the fortifications. The enemy commander would know where to bombard with his artillery and the weakest points for the infantry to attack.

I climbed back down to see Garcia in the cockpit, the engine was running and the blue flames from the stub exhausts were visible in the gloom. Garcia climbed out onto the wing beside the cockpit. He helped me do up the parachute straps and seat belts, and then jumped down. I checked the instruments and cocked the guns. I signalled for the chocks to be pulled away, opened the throttle to full power and emerged from the hide. The tail was up in seconds and the Fiat lifted off in a few more. I turned away to the north and climbed at full power into the eye of the sun.

The forest was a vivid green, the sky bluer than ever before, and the cloud on the horizon shone whiter.

A few minutes after take-off, I could see the Ospreys in the distance coming from the direction of the river. They were flying back and forward across the line of the trail at about 1,000 metres. I continued my climb at full power, keeping up-sun of the Bolivians. Soon I was at 1,500 metres. I saw the Ospreys straighten up and fly west, keeping just to the north of the trail. They were flying in loose formation with one aircraft trailing the leader out to his right and a little above him. I circled until they had passed me.

I levelled out, left the throttle at full power and dived towards the trailing aircraft, aiming to pull up under his tail, where his gunner could not bring his gun to bear. The speed increased until the slipstream and the exhaust noise were so loud as to create the illusion of profound silence.

Soon I was close enough to see the pilot and gunner and notice that both were looking at the ground. He was in a gentle turn to the right. I was pressed into my seat by the G-forces as I pulled up under him and matched his turn. I squeezed the trigger and four smoky white-and-red lines reached out. They passed above the aeroplane, and it pitched up suddenly and rolled into a steep turn to the right. I released the trigger, tightening my turn, to lead him, aiming above and in front. I corrected my aim and fired again. Smoky lines of burning phosphorus joined the two aircraft, bright white flashes covered his wings, tail and fuselage. He exploded.

I broke hard left and upward and passed through a cloud of flame and oily black smoke and pieces of wreckage. I could feel the heat and hear thumps as small pieces hit the Fiat. I completed my turn and could see the destroyed Osprey through streaks of oil on my windscreen. The ball of fire and smoke had pitched down into a vertical dive, shedding pieces of wreckage as it fell.

The second Osprey had turned away from me and was flying level. A thin trail of bluish smoke suggested that he was flying at full throttle. I still had some of the extra speed generated by the dive and turned towards him, slowly closing the distance. The aircraft was making a gentle turn to the right, enough to give his observer a clear shot at me but not enough to slow him down much. Tracers from the observer's gun flicked by. I fired, allowing for the distance and turn by aiming above and to his right. My tracers fell short, and I could see that he was drawing away slowly. I increased my lead and fired again. Flashes lit up the fuselage, the engine cowlings, the cockpits. He was on fire and trailing black smoke. I was gaining on him. A bright flame and dense black smoke enveloped him and trailed behind as he rolled smoothly to the left, his nose dropping until the machine was in a vertical dive. I turned left as hard as I could, pressed into the seat, head heavy, neck muscles taut, through the edge of the smoke and fire, circling back, seeing a parachute opening 300 metres below.

I was over thorn forest and several kilometres to the west of the fortin. I could see that the parachute was drifting further to the west and in a few seconds, he would be safe in Bolivian territory. I dived towards him, firing, correcting my aim, firing again, leaving his body dangling beneath his parachute, a smoky flare that had been a human being only a few seconds before.

Pillars of oily black smoke rose from the forest, where the remains of men who had loved and been loved were being consumed by fire.

I caught sight of a smoke trail in the corner of my eye. I turned steeply to the left and saw that it was coming from my aeroplane. Flames broke through the firewall in front of me. Smoke streamed past the cockpit and came up through the floor. I pulled up steeply, winding the trim hard forward. I flicked the seat harness buckle open, grabbed the ripcord of my parachute with my right hand and pushed the stick hard forward with my left.

The Fiat pitched down sharply, throwing me clear of the cockpit. I was free. My feet clipped the top of the rudder and sent me spinning as I pulled hard on the ripcord. The parachute opened with a bang, jerking me upright. I saw the thorn forest coming up and that my overalls were on fire. There was a flapping noise, I looked up. The parachute smouldered and two panels were ripped. A veil of smoke streamed past me. The forest was a blur. I held my knees and ankles together, pulled my elbows into my sides, buried my head in my hands, and closed my eyes.

About This Novel

This book is fiction and not history, but the fiction has been constructed within a non-fictional matrix, many of the characters lived and many of the events took place. Other events described took place too, but not in Paraguay or in 1932 or 1933.

Robert Herbert Scott was hanged for the murder of Gwendoline Kathleen Murray on 17 April 1924. I do not know who defended him, or anything about Gwendoline, except that she was twelve years old when she died, or whether Scott had a wife. A defendant's wife clung to my robes, in the corridor outside the High Court, after her husband was sentenced, repeating, 'But he hasn't done anything.' He had killed a man and been convicted of manslaughter. And he had done it before.

SS *Eden* of Campbell & Co. is fictional but is identical to SS *Ripple* of Richardson & Co. which traded around the coasts of New Zealand but never journeyed to Paraguay. The voyage of SS *Eden* is fictional.

The story of the motorist who was shot dead as a result of a defective rifle accidentally discharged from the back of a passing truck is true, and it was initially thought to be murder. The client suspected of murder is fictional. During the Great Depression in New Zealand, many of the unemployed wore sugar bags over their only suit of clothes, and at least one bank manager told a farming couple that they could get by with one toothbrush.

The foreign concessions in China existed, and they came into being in the way described.

Conditions at Puerto Pinasco, the massacre of workers in 1927, and the condition of the indigenous people were as described. Asunción, its buildings, streets, and people are represented as they were described by travellers in the 1920s and 1930s, viewed in photographs and in news films of the era. The murder trial in Asunción was observed by one of my sources, who witnessed it about the time Travis arrived.

The giant yacaré yrupe water lilies appear on the Rio Paraguay from time to time, including January 2018.

The history of Paraguay from 1811 to 1932, and the Gran Chaco Dispute which commenced in early 1932, are as factually accurate as I could make them. I have not attempted to provide a complete or balanced history and have included only facts that are relevant to the plot.

I invented Hacienda Shaw, Fortin X, and the flora surrounding them and the flora in which the Junkers F 13 is discovered. Sometimes I have invented topographical detail to support a striking image.

The couple whose marriage was war existed, the attempted murder, the acid throwing incident, and the two suicides are factual but took place in Argentina some decades after 1932. A New Zealand friend of mine was (at her suggestion) a wedding-night present.

In 1932, Paraguay communicated with the outside world by telegraph, rail, and steamer as described. There was no airline service. There were some charter flights from and to Argentina, and possibly Uruguay.

The Café Indio and Café Eiffel and their staff and patrons are figments of my imagination.

Some White Russian refugees emigrated to Paraguay in the wake of their defeat by the Reds in the Russian Civil War and many played an important part in Paraguay's war effort during the Gran Chaco War. Some of them died in the conflict, the first during the Battle of Boquerón, 10 to 29 September 1932.

The story of the origins and fates of Colonia Nueva Germania and Nueva Australia is true. The Bauhaus and the artists mentioned are factual.

The people, history and geography of New Zealand are as I know them.

The Instituto Geográfico de la Nacional República del Paraguay and its learned and charming Director are inventions. The maps, postage stamps, and press clipping that the Director shows Travis are real, as is the information he gives to Travis.

The quote from President Daniel Domingo Salamanca Urey of Bolivia is accurate. I invented the quote from General Kundt but everything I know about him suggests that he thought the war would be a walkover. I made up the newspaper quote about the death of Lieutenant Rojas Silver, but the events occurred as described and the tone is consistent with the outrage felt by Paraguayans over the incident.

The other quotes from newspapers are factual or edited versions of actual reports. The quote from a newspaper story about Travis and his father barnstorming around the South Island of New Zealand is fictional. Their fictional flight was inspired by the real-life activities of barnstormers who flew all over New Zealand in the years after the Great War. Many of those barnstormers flew the Avro 504K.

The Casado Company was a major landowner in the Chaco Boreal and owned the town and factory at Puerto Casado.

Oil was found in the eastern foothills of the Bolivian Andes before the Gran Chaco War. However, it is unlikely that Bolivia or Paraguay fought over the Chaco believing there was oil beneath its surface.

New Zealand's part in the Great War was as described. The school's Cadet Corps existed. The speech by the Rector of Otago Boys High School is an invention but is entirely consistent with contemporary interpretations of the Great War. The 'Book of the Dead' came into being years later and a page of it is read out to the Senior Assembly of the school in the Great Hall, every Tuesday.

Many of the characters mentioned are real. They include General Juan Belaieff, young Alfredo Stroessner Matiauda, President José Patricio Guggiari Corniglione, Arturo Bray, the Argentinian volunteer Doctor Carlos de Sanctis, and Rafael Franco. José Félix Estigarribia Insaurralde is not only a historical figure, but he is also possibly the most famous Paraguayan of all time. The quote at the start of Chapter Seven is an adaption of President Porfirio Díaz' of Mexico's aphorism, *so far from God, so close to the United States*. Estigarribia may well have agreed with the sentiment expressed in the invented quote. The details of Estigarribia and Kundt's careers down to 1932 are factual.

The historical characters' actions before the arrival of Travis are closely based on fact. I have invented their interactions with Travis, but I have tried to make their fictional acts consistent with what I know of their life stories. Some of the minor characters are based on real people.

The events after the Great War in East Prussia, the Baltic States, and Russia happened as described.

Aimé Félix Tschiffely did ride from Argentina to New York and Isidoro Larregui, the Basque of the Wheelbarrow, did push his wheelbarrow ten thousand or more kilometres, but not in 1932. I don't know if they passed through Paraguay. The stuffed remains of Tschiffely's horses, Gato and Mancha, and Larregui's first wheelbarrow, grace the halls of the Museo del Transporte de Luján in Luján, Argentina.

Will Scotland made the first aeroplane flight at Dunedin in New Zealand in 1914, exactly as described. Travis' brother is fictional, but the Royal Naval Air Service and the Royal Air Force operated Sopwith Triplanes and Sopwith Camels on the Western Front in the Great War. The Royal Air Force provided aircraft and men as part of British aid to White Russian forces in South Russia in 1919 to 1920. Several Red aeroplanes were shot down by RAF aircraft. The giant R-class aeroplanes flown by the Imperial German Air Service existed and bombed many targets in Eastern and Western Europe, including London.

The Morane-Saulnier MS 129, the Fiat CR20bis, and the other aeroplanes that Travis flies in Paraguay were operated by the Paraguayan Aviación en Campaña, and I have endeavoured to describe their characteristics accurately. A Curtiss Falcon reconnaissance–bomber was converted into a VIP transport in the way described. President Eusebio Ayala and other high officials were flown into the war zone on numerous occasions.

The layout and buildings at Ñu Guasú airfield, Asunción, are an invention but the real airfield was similar. The airfield outside Buenos Aires and the activities there are fictional but consistent with what I know about aviation in Argentina in 1932.

The Uruguayan Air Service operated the Great War fighters, the Nieuport 27 and Spad XIII, until the 1930s, and in 1931 a visiting British pilot was allowed to fly a Nieuport after a check-flight in a Morane-Saulnier. The quotes from the technical reports on the Junkers F 13, Junkers Junior, and the Fiat CR20bis are factual, although they have been edited.

The mysterious Junkers F 13, its mission and its cargo, are fictional, although a Bolivian F 13 disappeared during the war, and the wreckage and the bodies of the crew were not discovered by Paraguayan hunters until many years afterwards.

Land navigation is sometimes performed using beads and compass as described. The first Bolivian soldiers to reach Lake Pitiantuta across the featureless landscape of the Chaco, used handheld compasses and step counts recorded by knotting a cord.

Air navigation in the early 1930s, and for a long time afterwards, was mostly performed with the simple methods described. The RAF used Popham signalling panels, and message drops and pickups for air-to-ground messaging, and other air forces used similar systems. The RAF used zogging to communicate between aircraft in flight.

The tactics of aerial combat described by Travis are consistent with those taught by the RAF in the 1920s and 1930s.

The article describing the Stratus glider is fictional as is the chapter describing the building and flying of it. The Stratus is identical to the Slingsby T.31 Tandem Tutor. I learned to fly gliders on the T.31, did my first solo on it, and soared in ridge lift and thermals, earning my Fédération Aéronautique Internationale 'C' Certificate and badge. The technical details of soaring are as accurate as I can make them. In the 1920s and 1930s, Germany was the leading nation in the sport of gliding and many Germans and foreigners learned to soar at Rossitten in East-Prussia with the Rhön-Rossitten Gesellschaft.

The sack and water method is an efficient way to cool beer in a hot climate. Codes using identical books as keys are a practical way to encode and decode messages. The bar by the docks of Asunción is fictional but jars full of pickled onions and murky water sat on my Uncle Richard's kitchen counter throughout my childhood.

The Casado Railway and the autovia existed. The railway was an important means of transporting men and supplies to the zone of operations and evacuating the wounded. Occasionally, damaged aeroplanes were transported by railway and steamer to Asunción to be repaired. The ledger recording the Army's use of the railway existed and was part of the records of the Casado Company. The company charged the Army for the privilege of using the railway as the Army fought and died to protect the company's interests. The record-keeping employee and Travis' interaction with him are fiction.

The steamer service to and from Buenos Aires operated as described. Max Weber is fictional but his comments on the War of the 70, the ethics of arms manufacturers, and Paraguay's arms purchases are accurate. His casual racism is typical of the era. Father de Morais is fictional but based on a Catholic priest who ministered to indigenous peoples in the Chaco Boreal, and his comments on those peoples are consistent with what I have read of them. The descriptions of the activities of the Jesuits in the Spanish parts of colonial South America in the 1600s and 1700s are factual. La Santísima Trinidad de Paraná exists and looks very much as it is described in the novel.

A Paraguayan military man did shoot his neighbour's cow when it broke into the soldier's garden one time too many. During the First and Second World Wars, New Zealand soldiers often used the expression 'no names, no pack drill'.

The offender with the misplaced belief in his genius is a staple of conversations between criminal lawyers over a few drinks at the end of a week of trials. The Chinese businessman, his bodyguard, his enforcer, and the enforcer's attack dog existed and behaved in the way described in New Zealand in 2017. All the other legal anecdotes are true.

Many real-life coups, revolutions (and the Civil War of 1922 to 1923) occurred in Paraguay before and after 1932. The planned coup and the countercoup in 1932 are fictional, but many of the details are consistent with actual events in Paraguay, at other times. The motivation for the coup is fictional.

Photo reconnaissance and the creation of photomosaics were carried out as described and could be as important in fact as they are in fiction.

The military communiques quoted are as published, although some have been slightly altered for the sake of clarity. I have no record of Estigarribia using the words attributed to him at the start of Chapter Twelve but every officer who has experienced combat knows them to be true.

My description of the aftermath of the Battle of Boquerón is fictional but is consistent with that described in the histories of the war. The lake of butterflies is fiction, but the naturalist David Attenborough visited Paraguay in the early 1950s and wrote that there are blue butterflies in Paraguay that behave in the way described.

The description of the front page of *El Liberal*, reporting the victory at Boquerón in late September 1932, is accurate. The poem by Siegfried Sassoon and the extract from one by William Butler Yeats are accurate.

The account of the Germans flooding tunnels with poison gas in the Great War is factual. The words attributed to Generals Nathan Bedford Forrest and William Tecumseh Sherman are from the historical record.

TSS *Earnslaw* was sent in pieces by railway to Lake Wakatipu and still sails the lake. The German Army and Navy operated a fleet of warships on Lake Tanganyika during the Great War. They were railed to the lake in pieces and assembled on the shores of the lake. One of them remains in civilian service.

The Bolivian and Paraguayan strategies at the start of the Gran Chaco War are accurately described, as is the controversy in Paraguayan military and civilian circles over whether to fight inland or on the west bank of the Rio Paraguay.

The quote from the RAF manual at the start of Chapter Fifteen is part fact and part fiction, although it is entirely consistent with the RAF's tactics in air combat and the policy of killing enemy aircrew escaping from their disabled aircraft by parachute. The manual specifically directs that enemy observers parachuting from a destroyed observation balloon should be killed.

I have referred to more than a thousand photographs relevant to the story. They have provided many details that are not in the textual sources.

The campaign described in Chapters Fourteen and Fifteen is entirely a product of my imagination.

Select List of References

Books and Articles

Air Ministry. (1922). *Royal Air Force Flying Training Manual Part II: Applied Flying*. London: Air Ministry.

Air Ministry. (1928). *Royal Air Force Pocket Book*. London: HMSO.

Attenborough, David. (2017). *Adventures of a Young Naturalist: The Zoo Quest Expeditions*. London: Two Roads.

Bejarano, Ramón César. (1984). *Fortines Paraguayos y Bolivianos 1905–1932*. Asunción: Editorial Toledo.

Bernhardson, Wayne. (1999). *Argentina, Uruguay & Paraguay* (3rd ed.). London: Lonely Planet.

Brawer, Moshe. (Ed.). (1991). *Atlas of South America*. New York: Simon & Schuster.

Carver, Robert. (2007). *Paradise with Serpents*. London: Harper Perennial.

Conway, Carle. (1969). *The Joy of Soaring: A Training Manual*. Los Angeles: Soaring Society of America Inc.

De Uphaugh, Johnny. (October 2007). Brisfit to Baghdad. *Aeroplane*, *10*(414), 12–15.

De Quesada, A., & Jowett, P. (2011). *The Chaco War 1932–1935: South America's greatest modern conflict*. Oxford: Osprey Publishing.

Durrell, Gerald. (1958). *The Drunken Forest*. London: Rupert Hart-Davis.

Estigarribia, José Félix. (1950). *The Epic of the Chaco: Marshal Estigarribia's Memoirs of the Chaco War 1932–1935*. Austin, Texas: University of Texas Press.

Farcau, Bruce W. (1996). *The Chaco War. Bolivia and Paraguay, 1932–1935*. Westport, Connecticut: Praeger Publishers.

Ferguson, Gregor. (1987). *Coup d'Etat: A Practical Manual.* New York: Poole, Arms & Armour Press.

Gibson, Sir Christopher. (1948). *Enchanted Trails.* London: Museum Press.

Gimlette, John. (2003). *At the Tomb of the Inflatable Pig: Travels through Paraguay.* London: Hutchinson.

Hagedorn, Dan, & Sapienza, Antonio Luis. (1996). *Aircraft of the Chaco War 1928–1935.* Atglen, Pennsylvania: Schiffer Publishing.

Hanratty, Dennis M., Meditz, Sandra W., & Weil, Thomas E. (1988). *Paraguay: A Country Study.* Washington, DC: Federal Research Division, Library of Congress.

Harvie, E. F. (1966). *Venture the Far Horizon: The Pioneer Long Distance Flights in New Zealand.* Christchurch: Whitcombe & Tombs Ltd.

Hughes, Mathew. (April 2005). Logistics and the Chaco War: Bolivia versus Paraguay, 1932–35. *The Journal of Military History, 69*(2), 411–437.

Kelly G. G. (1963). *The Gun in the Case.* Wellington: Whitcombe & Tombs.

Kolinski, Charles J. (1973). *Historical Dictionary of Paraguay.* Metuchen, New Jersey: Scarecrow Press.

Kronfeld, Robert. (1932). *Kronfeld on Gliding and Soaring: The Story of Motorless Flight.* London: John Hamilton.

Lee, David. (1983). *Never Stop the Engine When it's Hot.* London: Thomas Harmsworth Publishing Co.

National Advisory Committee for Aeronautics. (1926). *Aircraft Circular No. 6: All-Metal Junkers Airplane Type F 13.* Washington, DC: NACA.

National Advisory Committee for Aeronautics. (1927). *Aircraft Circular No. 43: Fiat CR20 Pursuit Airplane.* Washington, DC: NACA.

National Advisory Committee for Aeronautics. (1930). *Aircraft Circular No. 118: The Junkers-Junior Light Airplane (German).* Washington, DC: NACA.

Nesbitt-Dufort, John. (1970). *Open Cockpit: Flying Pre-War Fighting and Training Aircraft*. London: Speed & Sport Publications Ltd.

Penrose, Harald. (1984). *Adventure with Fate*. Shrewsbury, England: Airlife Publishing Ltd.

Reichmann, Helmut. (1980). *Flying Sailplanes: A Practical Training Manual*. Pacific Palisades, California: Thomson Publications.

Robinson, Paul. (September 1999). Forgotten Victors: White Russian Officers in Paraguay during the Chaco War, 1932–35. *Journal of Slavic Military Studies*, *12*(3), 178–185.

Sapienza, Antonio. (2018). *The Chaco Air War 1932–1935: The First Modern Air War in South America*. Solihull, UK: Helion & Company.

Sapienza, Antonio Luis, & Martínez Peláez, José Luis. (2020). *The Chaco War: 1932–1935: Fighting in the Green Hell*. Solihull, UK: Helion & Company.

Smith, G. O. (Winter 1950–51). A New Basic Trainer. *Gliding*, (*1*)4, 182–184.

Stroud, John. (August–November 1981). Junkers F 13: The Pioneer from Dessau. *Air Enthusiast*, 16, 66–75.

Thompson, R. W. (1964). *An Echo of Trumpets*. London: George Allen & Unwin.

Quill, Jeffrey. (1985). *Spitfire*. London: Arrow Books.

Wewege-Smith, Thomas. (July 1936). I flew for Bolivia. *Air Stories*, *3*(1), 33–40.

Williams, Neil. (1977). *Airborne*. Shrewsbury, England: Airlife Publications.

Williams, Neil. (2012). *Aerobatics*. Ramsbury, England: Airlife Publishing Ltd.

Zook, David H. (1960). *The Conduct of the Chaco War*. New Haven, Connecticut: Bookman Associates.

Maps

International Travel Maps. *Paraguay* 1:800,000. (c. 2017). www.itmb.com
Plano de Asunción. 1:15,000. Asunción, Edición Libreria Nacional, 1928.

The David Rumsey Map Collection at:
https://www.davidrumsey.com/.

Contains high-resolution scans of topographical maps covering all of Bolivia and Paraguay and many maps of historical interest.

Many of the books noted above have good maps of Paraguay in peace and war. Those authored by Attenborough, Bejarano, Farcau, Sapienza and Martinez, and Zook are particularly useful.

Newspapers

Newspapers were sourced from the following archives:
https://www.britishnewspaperarchive.co.uk/
https://paperspast.natlib.govt.nz/newspapers

Photographs

Many of the photographs I have referred to are to be found on these Facebook pages:

Aprendiendo del la Guerra Del Chaco (1932-1935).
El Paraguay Histórico.
Fotos Antiguas de la Ciudad de Asunción.
Guerra en El Desierto Paraguayo (1932-1935).
Memorias de la Guerra Del Chaco.

ACKNOWLEDGEMENTS

A special thanks to Sue Cheer who spent many hours reviewing the first and second drafts and made valuable suggestions large and small. David Tasker and Kit McCready read the manuscript and made useful comments. Antonio Luis Sapienza Fracchia is the author or co-author of several important books on the Gran Chaco war. He also answered many questions and provided important details. Antonio's friend Renato Angulo helped clarify some political history. Nelson Garcia of the Fundación Huellas de la Cultura Paraguaya was very helpful and his contributions included high-definition scans of useful maps. Monsignor John Harrison clarified a theological point. Errol Martyn loaned technical manuals. Steve Heyen produced the cover illustration, designed the cover and was a pleasure to work with. Marko from Speedprint fine-tuned the cover. Renell Judais did a painstaking copy edit.

Printed in Great Britain
by Amazon